# THE
# GARDENING
# PUZZLE BOOK

THE GARDENING PUZZLE BOOK

Research by Joe Varley

An Hachette UK Company
www.hachette.co.uk

Summersdale Publishers Ltd
Part of Octopus Publishing Group Limited
Carmelite House
50 Victoria Embankment
LONDON
EC4Y 0DZ
UK

www.summersdale.com

Printed and bound in Poland

ISBN: 978-1-80007-172-8

Substantial discounts on bulk quantities of Summersdale books are available to corporations, professional associations and other organizations. For details contact general enquiries by telephone: +44 (0) 1243 771107 or email: enquiries@summersdale.com

# THE
# GARDENING
# PUZZLE BOOK

## 200 BRAIN-TEASING
## ACTIVITIES

FELICITY HART

summersdale

# INTRODUCTION

If you've picked up this book, it's fair to say you're fond of a bit of gardening. Whether you use expert knowledge and skills learned over a lifetime or just potter about in a garden shed now and then, there's nothing like some green-fingered activity to keep your mind and body active.

If you think you know your chrysanthemums from your carnations, or your geraniums from your gladioli, *The Gardening Puzzle Book* will keep you entertained for hours. It features an eclectic mix of conundrums, including crosswords, word searches, sudokus, anagrams and plenty of trivia questions to nourish and challenge horticultural brains.

What could be better than sitting in your garden, taking in the beautiful array of plants and flowers, and opening up this carefully cultivated collection of garden-inspired puzzles? I hope *The Gardening Puzzle Book* proves a welcome addition to every gardener's bookshelf.

# WORD SEARCH: IN THE HERB GARDEN

```
J  H  G  A  A  H  A  V  H  G  T  R  L  D  G
J  A  C  H  E  R  V  I  L  D  E  I  Y  T  B
H  U  J  A  N  B  A  Y  L  K  S  G  T  A  D
P  A  R  S  L  E  Y  P  G  A  J  J  U  R  G
V  C  F  H  C  M  P  L  B  H  C  F  D  R  A
A  S  Y  H  B  O  J  A  N  B  V  C  F  A  U
Y  N  H  M  J  K  R  O  R  F  D  X  P  G  B
H  T  F  C  D  E  T  I  V  C  T  Y  H  O  J
I  T  M  A  R  J  O  R  A  M  H  N  M  N  R
F  X  S  A  F  E  D  V  A  N  H  B  U  I  M
B  F  G  P  M  T  E  A  F  M  D  N  B  D  R
W  P  H  Y  T  K  G  F  E  N  N  E  L  F  J
M  K  H  L  M  H  B  V  R  E  S  A  R  Y  H
V  T  T  F  J  U  N  K  M  H  F  R  O  I  K
H  E  A  B  R  F  D  R  O  S  E  M  A  R  Y
```

Find the following flavourings in the grid.

| | | |
|---|---|---|
| PARSLEY | MARJORAM | BASIL |
| TARRAGON | ROSEMARY | CORIANDER |
| THYME | CHERVIL | FENNEL |

# CROSSWORD: FLOWERS & PLANTS

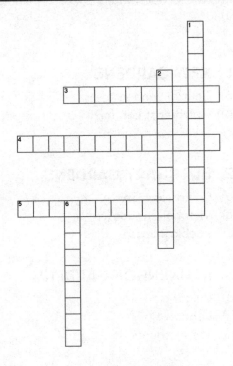

## ACROSS

**3.** A shy person (10)

**4.** Japan's national flower (13)

**5.** Fastest legume? (6, 4)

## DOWN

**1.** Primate brainteaser (6, 6)

**2.** Request to amnesiac? (6-2-3)

**6.** Genus of plant that includes the daffodil – fell in love with himself (9)

# TRIVIA

Can you name the location where these well-known gardens are to be found?

### 1. KEW GARDENS

a) Central London
b) North-east London
c) South-west London

### 2. BUTCHART GARDENS

a) California, USA
b) Victoria, Canada
c) Puebla, Mexico

### 3. KEUKENHOF GARDENS

a) Bulgaria
b) Lithuania
c) The Netherlands

### 4. BLENHEIM PALACE GARDENS

a) Oxfordshire
b) Bedfordshire
c) Berkshire

# PAIRS GAME

Match up the 20 flowers in 20 seconds. The first one has been done for you.

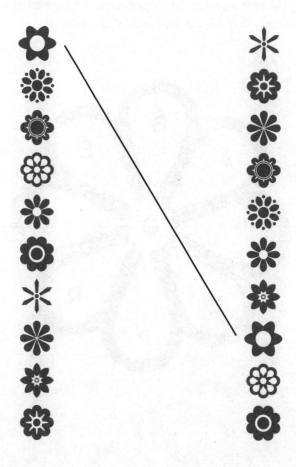

# WORD FLOWER

Attention, quizzing gardeners! See how many words of four or more letters you can make from the letters below. All words must include the central letter, and proper nouns don't count! Also, can you find a word that uses all the letters?

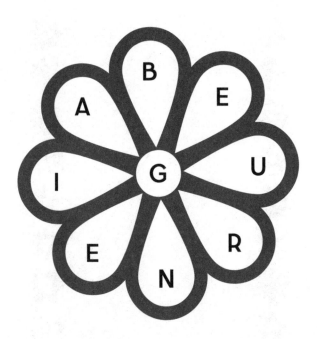

# MAZE

Can you get through this hedge maze from top to bottom in under 30 seconds?

# ANAGRAMS: GARDENING TOOLS

Rearrange these letters to spell out the names of some typical gardening implements.

GRESN HAIRS PUN

O AS WITH GREEN

HERBAL ROWWE

WAND R HOTEL

ELBOW F REAL

# WORD LADDER

Roses are among the best-loved flowers in the world, and they are bought and sold in the millions. In this word ladder, change one letter at a time to turn the word "sale" into "rose".

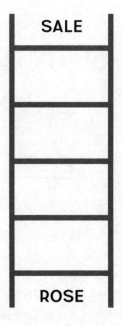

SALE

ROSE

# CROSSWORD: TYPES OF PLANTS

## ACROSS

**3.** Watch out for spines! (6)

**4.** Panda fodder (6)

**5.** Living for several years (9)

**6.** Thrives in mountainous climates (6)

## DOWN

**1.** Conquers ascent of mountain (7)

**2.** Moist and juicy? (9)

# COUNTING CONUNDRUM

$$\text{shovel} + \text{shovel} + \text{shovel} = 60$$

$$\text{shovel} + \text{plant} + \text{plant} = 30$$

$$\text{plant} - \text{watering can} = 3$$

$$\text{shovel} + \text{plant} + \text{watering can} = ?$$

# RIDDLE

A popular item of produce is the answer to this riddle.

*My first is in apple and also in pear*
*My second is in orange but not in lime*
*My third is in stem but not in leaf*
*My fourth is in bean and also in pea*
*My fifth is in carrot but not in parsnip*
*My sixth is in beetroot but not in lettuce*

**What am I?**

# WORD SEARCH: EAT YOUR GREENS

```
H  B  A  O  E  T  S  Q  M  Q  A  L  J  K  F
P  D  Q  R  C  Y  K  Y  K  J  X  A  P  N  L
S  M  I  D  T  P  M  V  C  A  B  B  A  G  E
U  A  U  T  L  I  X  H  G  O  K  R  R  U  T
G  S  Q  F  J  M  C  B  K  H  F  O  T  T  T
A  L  Z  E  O  A  V  H  U  U  P  C  S  J  U
R  B  M  I  N  C  Z  A  O  Q  F  C  B  E  C
A  D  W  I  V  H  I  A  O  K  R  O  P  V  E
P  N  P  A  O  H  M  X  R  G  E  L  O  E  W
S  S  G  C  Y  A  S  C  U  E  R  I  C  O  T
A  D  T  H  U  X  Z  O  Q  K  A  V  L  Z  J
W  L  W  J  H  S  M  Z  K  L  J  J  S  B  L
T  T  V  G  O  M  X  K  Z  R  D  A  A  W  S
L  D  Q  M  G  L  I  L  U  K  A  L  E  H  C
G  W  N  A  E  B  N  E  E  R  G  A  G  K  A
```

Find the following healthy foods in the grid.

| | | |
|---|---|---|
| BROCCOLI | SPINACH | ASPARAGUS |
| KALE | OKRA | CABBAGE |
| ARTICHOKE | GREEN BEAN | LETTUCE |

# ACROSTICS

Solve the clues correctly and the shaded squares will reveal a common shrub. What is it?

1. Performance dance
2. Rocket take-off
3. Greek god
4. Sturgeon roe
5. Young cat

# TRIVIA

1. According to *Guinness World Records*, the longest line of garden flamingos comprised how many of the pink ornamentals?

   a) 1,496
   b) 3,753
   c) 11,371

2. The world's largest flower architectural structure was covered in how many pots containing flowers?

   a) 12,000
   b) 56,500
   c) 74,000

# GARDENING WORDS

The gardening world is full of wonderful words, but do you know the meaning of the following?

### 1. CHIT

a) To hack or cut
b) To encourage a potato tuber to grow
c) A species of fungus

### 2. SUCKER

a) A flower that is resistant to bacterial infection
b) A type of small hand tool
c) A shoot that arises from roots

### 3. TILTH

a) A collection of dead leaves
b) A fine crumbly layer of soil
c) A family of earthworms

# SPOT THE
# DIFFERENCE

Can you spot the five differences between the two pictures?

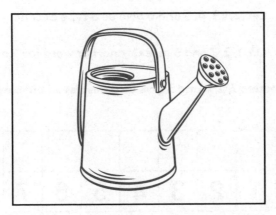

# WORD GROWER

The letters of a seven-letter word have been numbered 1 to 7. Solve the clues to reveal a plant that is used as a flavouring.

**Letters 5, 4, 3 and 6 give us a type of cone.**

**Letters 4, 3, 1, 2, 7 and 6 give us another word for "to harm".**

**Letters 7, 2, 4 and 3 give us a destroyed building.**

| | | | | | | |
|---|---|---|---|---|---|---|
| 1 | 2 | 3 | 4 | 5 | 6 | 7 |

# MYSTERY SUDOKU

Complete the grid so that every row, column and 3 × 3 box contains the letters DREWFOLSC in any order. One row or column contains something (seven letters) found in many gardens.

|   |   | R | E |   |   |   |   | C |
|---|---|---|---|---|---|---|---|---|
|   | C |   |   | D |   | L | E |   |
|   | S |   |   | C |   | R |   |   |
|   | W |   | S |   | D |   |   |   |
|   |   | O |   | L |   | W |   |   |
|   | O |   | E |   |   | C |   |   |
|   | D | F |   | S | W |   | O |   |
|   | W |   |   |   |   | F |   |   |

# BETWEEN THE LINES

Something that is used by many gardeners can be inserted in the blank line so that, reading downwards, seven three-letter words are formed. What is the hidden word between the lines?

| A | D | E | A | R | U | A |
|---|---|---|---|---|---|---|
|   |   |   |   |   |   |   |
| T | G | U | E | B | E | E |

# MISSING WORDS

Fill in the blank spaces to make two compound words or phrases.

| Bone | | Fat |
|------|---|------|
| Chick | | Shoot |
| Crazy | | Stone |

# WORD SEARCH: IN BLOOM

| | | | | | | | | | | | | | |
|---|---|---|---|---|---|---|---|---|---|---|---|---|---|
| B | O | Y | R | W | M | C | T | H | G | P | C | P | E | R |
| M | E | L | V | M | U | O | D | P | H | K | Q | O | M | G |
| P | L | G | L | B | D | S | C | L | V | P | S | C | E | J |
| B | J | V | O | K | E | M | E | E | O | A | V | R | Z | V |
| I | V | B | U | N | S | O | V | L | L | G | A | H | X | O |
| V | E | E | T | Y | I | S | W | O | I | N | I | H | U | Y |
| Z | W | O | B | H | D | A | I | E | I | H | T | R | I | K |
| D | O | W | O | P | C | V | K | U | D | Z | R | I | A | T |
| W | N | F | M | T | S | U | M | M | Y | C | X | V | H | M |
| M | E | W | Z | G | X | G | H | L | I | S | J | N | M | C |
| M | U | I | M | A | L | Y | L | B | S | X | E | E | V | V |
| Q | P | Z | I | N | N | I | A | Q | Y | A | C | C | T | S |
| C | S | U | N | E | G | I | R | R | D | J | T | Q | S | K |
| Y | I | F | D | K | S | L | N | J | A | S | T | E | R | D |
| O | W | L | K | K | R | U | M | R | N | L | P | T | E | L |

Find the following colourful flowers in the grid.

| | | |
|---|---|---|
| ASTER | GERANIUM | SEDUM |
| BEGONIA | LAMIUM | VIOLA |
| COSMOS | MARIGOLD | ZINNIA |

# CROSSWORD: GARDEN VISITORS MAMMALS

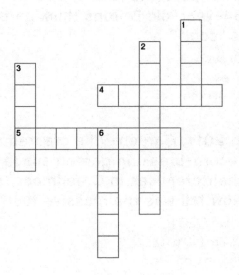

## ACROSS

**4.** Mammal with distinctive black and white face (6)

**5.** Member of the family *Sciuridae* (8)

## DOWN

**1.** Mammal leaves annoying mounds (4)

**2.** Mrs Tiggy-Winkle (8)

**3.** Field or house? (5)

**6.** Hopping buck or doe (6)

# TRIVIA

1.  **According to the results from a 2021 poll, as printed in the *Independent*, what percentage of 2,000 18- to 34-year-old Britons think gardening is "cool"?**

a) 24 per cent
b) 51 per cent
c) 83 per cent

2.  **In 2014, Garden-Ville created a record-breaking garden spade at their premises in Creedmoor, Texas. How tall was the massive tool?**

a) 6.8 m (22.3 ft)
b) 12.4 m (40.6 ft)
c) 56.5 m (185.3 ft)

# PAIRS GAME

Match up the 20 birds in 20 seconds. The first one has been done for you.

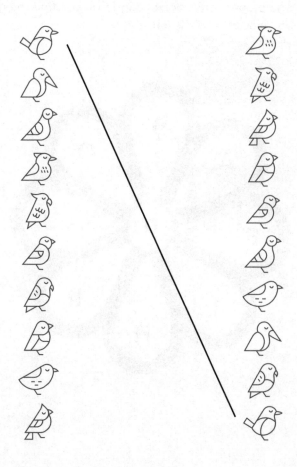

# WORD FLOWER

See how many words of four or more letters you can make from the letters below. All words must include the central letter, and proper nouns don't count! Can you find the name of a plant that uses all the letters?

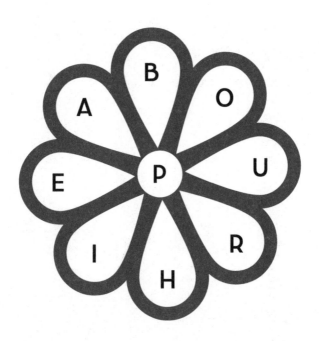

# MAZE

Can you get through this hedge maze from left to right in under 30 seconds?

# ANAGRAMS: GENERA

Rearrange these letters to reveal genera of the family *Iridaceae*.

### OCC URS

### FISE EAR

### GISOL DUAL

# WORD LADDER

Palms evoke tropical gardens and are a firm favourite among gardeners. In this word ladder, change one letter at a time to turn the word "hall" into "palm".

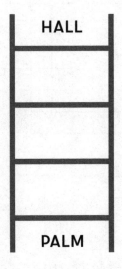

HALL

PALM

# CROSSWORD: ANIMAL MAGIC

The plant-related answers to the clues below all contain the name of an animal.

## ACROSS

**3.** Man's best friend in small forest (7)

**4.** Palm with long hairstyle (8)

**6.** Crustacean plus fruit (4, 5)

## DOWN

**1.** Mitten for vulpine? (8)

**2.** Large farm animal loses footing (7)

**5.** Pinch a feline? (6)

# COUNTING CONUNDRUM

🛻 + 🛻 = 14

🛒 + 🚧 = 18

🛒 + 🛻 = 13

🛒 = ?  🛻 = ?  🚧 = ?

# WORD LINK

Each of the three words in the clues below have a word in common. For example, if the clues were "count", "faith" and "weight", the answer would be "lose" (lose count, lose faith and lose weight). Answer each of the following clues correctly to reveal a word in the shaded column, which is something regularly used by gardeners.

1. plan, war, theory
2. blue, new, harvest
3. eyed, sparrow, bit
4. pressure, review, group
5. wine, hole, free

| 1. | | | |
| 2. | | | |
| 3. | | | |
| 4. | | | |
| 5. | | | |

32

# WORD SEARCH: KNOW YOUR ONIONS

```
O V M G M T P D P H E U O B P
V N X W O I O N G L K G K U Z
M V I R Y N T J O D O D N J I
I T R O B F A V L P H P O S A
C A E V N K T A U W C V O I S
C C E D O B O M O J I D L H Z
V A W R F C P R I Y T N Y R Q
V B U N E K T Y Y G R H Z P Q
K D V C I W T O L L A H S T O
J S D N V E P T C D N Q I R T
G C K B S S E H A D N Z Q S U
W S M D U J H L E E K Q M F R
X F K R D L O X Z A O M F S N
H Q J R L J P P Y Y L P Q W I
D S W E D E Q T Z L I D A S P
```

Find the following vegetables in the grid.

| ARTICHOKE | ONION | SHALLOT |
| CARROT | POTATO | SWEDE |
| LEEK | PUMPKIN | TURNIP |

# ACROSTICS

Solve the clues correctly and the shaded squares will reveal a poisonous plant. What is it?

1. Narrative poetry often put to music
2. Early stage of organism development
3. Cube of fatty meat
4. Period of learning
5. Roman goddess of dawn

| 1. | | | | | |
|----|----|----|----|----|----|
| 2. | | | | | |
| 3. | | | | | |
| 4. | | | | | |
| 5. | | | | | |

# TRIVIA

1. **In 2020, Kevin Nicks claimed the world record for the fastest motorized garden shed. What speed did he attain?**

a) 106 mph (171 km/h)
b) 174 mph (280 km/h)
c) 199 mph (320 km/h)

2. **Snails can be the bane of a gardener's life, but the common garden snail is generally considered to be the fastest snail species. Over a 31-cm (12.2-in.) course in the USA in 1990, a snail named Verne completed the distance in how many minutes?**

a) 1 minute 2 seconds
b) 1 minute 39 seconds
c) 2 minutes 13 seconds

# GARDENING WORDS

Landscape gardening is big business. Well, who wouldn't want their garden to look its best? The following are terms commonly used by landscape gardeners, but do you know their meaning?

### 1. ALLEE

a) An artificial shrub or bush, used in garden design
b) A type of circular saw, usually used for cutting patio paving
c) A pathway or walkway, usually bordered by hedges, trees or bamboo

### 2. DRY-LAID

a) A stone path built without concrete
b) A garden stake installed without the help of water
c) Flagstones with a maximum 25 per cent water composition

### 3. MOONGATE

a) An artificial, shimmering illumination, usually used at night
b) Any crescent-shaped garden design
c) A circular aperture in a fence or wall

# SPOT THE DIFFERENCE

Can you spot the five differences between the two pictures?

# WORD GROWER

The letters of a seven-letter word have been numbered 1 to 7. Solve the clues to reveal a well-known garden plant.

**Letters 6, 4 and 5 give us a charged particle.**

**Letters 3, 4 and 7 give us an Indian state.**

**Letters 1, 6 and 3 give us a Tom Hanks film.**

**Letters 7, 2, 4 and 5 give us a long period of time.**

| | | | | | | |
|---|---|---|---|---|---|---|
| 1 | 2 | 3 | 4 | 5 | 6 | 7 |

# MYSTERY SUDOKU

Complete the grid so that every row, column and 3 × 3 box contains the letters ADORBGINS in any order. One row or column contains an eight-letter word that is something heard in many a garden.

| | | I | R | | | | | |
|---|---|---|---|---|---|---|---|---|
| | | A | | | S | I | | |
| I | D | | | | | | O | |
| | | I | | | | | R | |
| N | O | | | | | | | B |
| A | R | | | | | | | N |
| | | R | | | A | | B | |
| D | | | R | O | | G | | |
| | S | | G | I | | A | | |

# BETWEEN THE LINES

A small creature found in gardens can be inserted in the blank line so that, reading downwards, eight three-letter words are formed. What is the hidden creature between the lines?

| E | D | O | B | E | T | A | A |
|---|---|---|---|---|---|---|---|
|   |   |   |   |   |   |   |   |
| K | Y | E | E | B | N | C | D |

# HIDDEN TOOLS

In each of the sentences below, a gardening tool is hidden. For instance, in the sentence "In Soho every street has a story to tell", the word "hoe" is hidden in "So**ho e**very".

1. You can either leave the item on the shelf or keep it in the drawer.

2. Rosario says she arson-proofed the letterbox using tried-and-tested methods.

3. The agency made sure that the video intro welcomed everybody to the session.

4. I ordered Keira kebab and chips while she was on the phone to Joe.

5. The feedback form began with the following question: "Did you find your day at the spa delightful?"

# WORD SEARCH: LET IT GROW

```
N Z U G L J B P M S B M Z J P
P E O G P X T B U C Y E I Q H
O W G L X W G R I L H D N G U
V C P O C V O V S R T X C X G
C M A A R H L E S P O S A Q Z
Z K J L P T E U A A M T M L M
H Q L S C Y I Y T J O C A G M
I Q O Y E I Q N O I E D R A Z
W H A X G S U L P H U R G N D
P P J H O W R M M B K N R Q A
I Q X B F P S C U X E P H E P
U Y S O N J K E W S L O D K K
I B J R E K U T I J O Y V W W
T J B O V Q B U S O U D R M D
L A F N I F M C H L O R I D E
```

Find the following substances found in garden fertilizers.

| | | |
|---|---|---|
| NITROGEN | SULPHUR | MAGNESIUM |
| POTASSIUM | CALCIUM | CHLORIDE |
| PHOSPHORUS | BORON | ZINC |

# CROSSWORD: HERBS

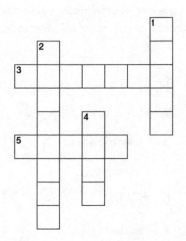

## ACROSS

**3.** According to Ogden Nash, this is "gharsley" (7)

**5.** Traditional male Christian name (5)

## DOWN

**1.** This flies when you're having fun (5)

**2.** One for aniseed lovers (8)

**4.** Herb belonging to the celery family (4)

# TRIVIA

The Royal Society for the Prevention of Accidents certainly has its work cut out. Each year in the UK approximately 300,000 people are injured in their gardens severely enough to require hospital treatment. More than a third are children, and 87,000 people are injured actively gardening. Put these garden tools in order of the most injuries caused.

1. Shears

2. Hoses and sprinklers

3. Lawnmowers

4. Flowerpots

5. Spades

6. Garden forks

7. Secateurs and pruners

8. Garden canes and sticks

9. Electric hedge trimmers

10. Plant tubs and troughs

# PAIRS GAME

Match up the 20 leaves in 20 seconds. The first one has been done for you.

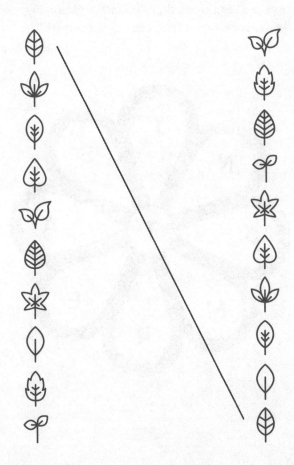

# WORD FLOWER

See how many words of four or more letters you can make from the letters below. All words must include the central letter, and proper nouns don't count! Additionally, can you find a flavoursome word that uses all the letters?

# MAZE

Can you get through this hedge maze from top to bottom in under 30 seconds?

# ANAGRAMS: FRUITY

Rearrange these letters to reveal types of fruit.

LUMP

O VILE

RUCEC BUM

NER GOA

# WORD LADDER

In this word ladder, starting with the word "jest", change one letter at a time to turn the word into "hose" – a useful gardening item.

JEST

HOSE

# CROSSWORD: GARDEN VISITORS INVERTEBRATES

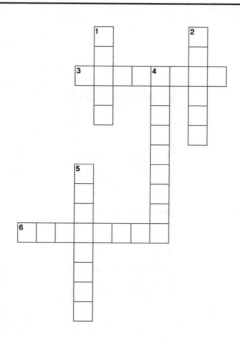

## ACROSS

**3.** Small flying beetle, often spotted (8)

**6.** Aphid (8)

## DOWN

**1.** Common gastropod (5)

**2.** Hearing organ plus fake hair (6)

**4.** Flits to dairy? (9)

**5.** Sweet pollen collector (8)

# COUNTING CONUNDRUM

☀ + ☀ + ☀ = 30

☀ + 🐦 + 🐦 = 18

🐦 − 🏠 = 2

🏠 + (☀ × 🐦) = ?

# RIDDLE

The following clues will reveal an
ornamental gardening technique.

*My first is in plant and also in petal*
*My second is in hose, but not in shears*
*My third is in planter, but not in trug*
*My fourth is in wire and also in snail*
*My fifth is in water, but not in pond*
*My sixth is in roots, but not in stems*
*My seventh is in lily, but not in daisies*

**What am I?**

# WORD SEARCH: SCIENTIFICALLY SPEAKING

```
C H G V J V M P L I T S I P D
L H Y U W T Z E A K F R X L M
K Q L U K H U C G C N U L E C
F M T O M U I B M A C L L P T
O Q I B R C R P A T S S E R E
B T G Y U O V L N Y C P R A J
W N Q O U P P W W A G Y O C T
J M L L M N Y H A V V N J R C
J H Q E K C A W Y B U Y C F E
S Q L N P M O M I L D N X D E
A Y E U G S Y F Z O L R M X O
X O L I A H V S T A M E N H C
C N T Q J J Y O G P G P K J C
G S L V N V U U G G C U N Y A
K L M E B X Y P H L O E M B Q
```

The following words relate to the science of botany –
find as many as you can.

CHLOROPHYLL      CAMBIUM      STIGMA

PHLOEM      PISTIL      STAMEN

XYLEM      CARPEL      MEGASPORE

# ACROSTICS

Solve the clues correctly and the shaded squares will reveal a type of buttercup that shares its name with a fairy-tale character. What is it?

1. Worldwide
2. English name for Portuguese city
3. Relating to milk
4. Small African antelope
5. Stupid people (plural)

| 1. | | | | | |
|----|---|---|---|---|---|
| 2. | | | | | |
| 3. | | | | | |
| 4. | | | | | |
| 5. | | | | | |

# TRIVIA

Have you ever wondered how many trees there are on Earth? Of course, it's impossible to come up with an exact figure. However, for the first time, the Botanic Gardens Conservation International has presented an overview of all known tree species by scientific name and country-level distribution via its database GlobalTreeSearch. Without the assistance of the database, can you guess how many species of tree are currently known to science?

a) 25,505

b) 60,065

c) 122,100

# GARDENING WORDS

Some of the smallest words can be the trickiest to understand, and this applies in the world of gardening. Try to correctly identify the meaning of the following.

### 1. WEED

a) A plant that grows and dies twice annually
b) Any plant growing in the wrong place
c) Any plant that steals another plant's nutrition

### 2. DIBBER

a) A tiny metal disc used as a marker in gardening
b) A small wooden stick for making holes in the ground
c) A screwdriver-like tool used in garden woodwork, especially fencing

### 3. RILL

a) A small support for climbing plants
b) A narrow watercourse, especially for aesthetic garden features
c) Tiny soil-munching organisms, similar to termites

# SPOT THE DIFFERENCE

Can you spot the five differences between the two pictures?

# WORD GROWER

The letters of an eight-letter word have been numbered 1 to 8. Solve the clues to reveal a type of aggregate sometimes used in heavy-duty gardening.

**Letters 3, 6 and 5 give us a large mythical bird.**

**Letters 7, 8 and 4 give us a primary colour.**

**Letters 5, 1, 2, 3 and 4 give us a green leafy vegetable.**

| | | | | | | | |
|---|---|---|---|---|---|---|---|
| 1 | 2 | 3 | 4 | 5 | 6 | 7 | 8 |

# MYSTERY SUDOKU

Complete the grid so that every row, column and 3 × 3 box contains the letters BRUTALWOE in any order. One row or column contains a six-letter word that is a vital gardening implement.

| | | L | | | O | | | |
|---|---|---|---|---|---|---|---|---|
| T | | | W | | | | | |
| | | B | U | R | | W | | |
| | | R | | | E | | L | |
| | L | U | | | | A | E | |
| | T | | R | | | U | | |
| | A | | W | U | L | | | |
| | | | | B | | | | U |
| | | | E | | | T | | |

# BETWEEN THE LINES

An acid-loving plant can be inserted in the blank line so that, reading downwards, seven three-letter words are formed. What is the hidden word between the lines?

| S | T | R | A | S | B | A |
|---|---|---|---|---|---|---|
|   |   |   |   |   |   |   |
| Y | A | M | E | E | T | T |

# MISSING PLANT

Insert the name of a plant so that, reading downwards, five five-letter words are formed. What is the plant?

| S | C | T | L | P |
|---|---|---|---|---|
| L | I | R | O | R |
|   |   |   |   |   |
| S | A | M | E | S |
| H | R | P | R | S |

# WORD SEARCH: GARDEN CRITTERS

| | | | | | | | | | | | | | |
|---|---|---|---|---|---|---|---|---|---|---|---|---|---|
| C | T | V | D | Q | L | E | E | B | P | D | E | L | M | U |
| G | F | U | E | X | P | Y | T | T | J | R | S | A | L | V |
| I | U | T | U | X | A | Z | X | R | H | R | L | D | D | Y |
| Y | N | B | U | T | T | E | R | F | L | Y | N | Y | O | R |
| F | Z | F | U | S | S | O | T | R | I | E | Z | B | K | A |
| R | U | G | G | Q | M | R | O | W | A | N | N | I | R | L |
| G | W | R | Z | G | F | L | D | D | N | F | O | R | X | L |
| V | C | C | F | V | W | L | P | T | S | C | B | D | L | I |
| O | B | O | G | Y | A | J | J | T | P | Q | V | Z | P | P |
| N | V | E | P | T | N | P | D | S | K | S | K | D | C | R |
| K | D | P | E | B | W | W | H | A | P | A | W | K | U | E |
| Z | A | I | E | T | O | I | A | I | Y | W | T | T | C | T |
| E | I | G | M | G | L | W | D | Q | D | Z | K | Y | W | A |
| D | Y | B | C | I | D | E | H | P | Q | Z | E | L | H | C |
| A | T | Y | C | K | R | T | W | V | I | D | H | E | H | P |

In the grid, find the following creatures commonly seen in gardens.

| | | |
|---|---|---|
| BEE | WORM | SNAIL |
| CATERPILLAR | BUTTERFLY | LADYBIRD |
| BEETLE | APHID | SPIDER |

# CROSSWORD: GARDEN FEATURES

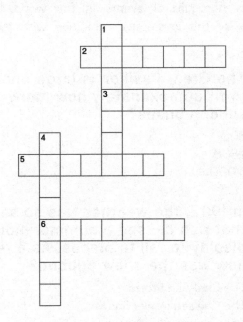

## ACROSS

**2.** Open-air porch, roofed (7)

**3.** Pavilion structure (6)

**5.** Practice of cutting trees and shrubs into defined shapes (7)

**6.** Wood, bamboo or metal lattice (7)

## DOWN

**1.** Outdoor roofed feature offering shade (7)

**4.** Water squirter (8)

# TRIVIA

The Chelsea Flower Show is one of the most famous and prestigious horticultural events in the world. Test your knowledge of this impressive exhibition with these three questions.

**1. The Great Pavilion is large enough to fit approximately how many London buses?**

a) 500
b) 1,500
c) 3,000

**2. In 1932, the weather was so severe that rain caused a summer-house display to fall to pieces. As a result, how was the show dubbed?**

a) The Chel-Sea Storm
b) The Chelsea Power Shower
c) The Chelsea Shower Flow

**3. One memorable bloom in 2017 was named after and presented to which actress?**

a) Dame Maggie Smith
b) Dame Judi Dench
c) Dame Helen Mirren

# PAIRS GAME

Match up the 20 potted plants in 20 seconds. The first one has been done for you.

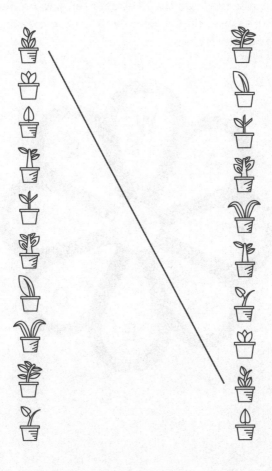

# WORD FLOWER

Attention, quizzing gardeners! See how many words of four or more letters you can make from the letters below. All words must include the central letter, and proper nouns don't count! Also, find a word with a nautical connection that uses all the letters!

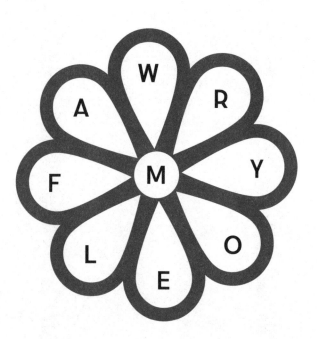

# MAZE

Can you get from the top to the middle of this hedge maze in under 30 seconds?

# ANAGRAMS: A LITTLE HELP

Rearrange these letters to reveal insects that can be beneficial to gardens.

LEB TEE

PED SIR

FOV HERYL

LANCE WIG

# WORD LADDER

If you have a knack for solving word ladders, you shouldn't have to make a "meal" of this! Change one letter at a time to turn the word "meal" into "leaf".

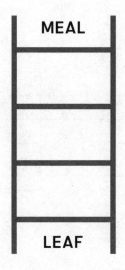

MEAL

LEAF

# CROSSWORD: POPULAR FLOWERS

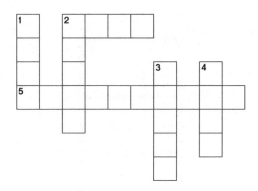

## ACROSS

**2.** Girl's name (4)

**5.** Mythical animal plays card game? (10)

## DOWN

**1.** Structure found in the eye (4)

**2.** Light purple (5)

**3.** Popular for making chains (5)

**4.** Among thorns (4)

# COUNTING CONUNDRUM

 +  = 13

 ×  = 42

 −  = 1

 = ?     = ?

# MINI SUDOKU: SPRING

Spring is a magical season for gardeners. Here's a chance to enjoy spring in another way by completing the grid so that every row, column and 2 × 3 box contains the letters that make up the word "spring".

| R |   |   |   |   |   |
|---|---|---|---|---|---|
|   | S | P |   |   |   |
| I |   |   | G |   |   |
|   | N |   |   |   | R |
|   |   |   | P | S |   |
|   |   |   |   | G |   |

# WORD SEARCH: HOUSING PLANTS

| K | H | G | U | O | R | T | Z | M | E | H | F | I | Z | F |
|---|---|---|---|---|---|---|---|---|---|---|---|---|---|---|
| V | E | C | R | U | V | Y | X | E | F | N | K | D | F | N |
| V | S | I | K | D | T | X | U | J | Z | T | F | X | K | O |
| S | D | I | Y | T | G | I | F | O | O | C | P | X | G | G |
| H | H | Z | L | G | I | L | J | P | S | K | R | K | O | Y |
| Z | B | P | E | L | W | K | E | T | S | Y | A | C | J | B |
| M | V | O | Q | E | R | H | K | R | P | I | C | K | Q | K |
| R | S | Z | X | Z | C | G | O | K | R | Y | W | X | F | O |
| P | B | B | H | A | J | S | T | O | G | A | J | P | B | P |
| M | Q | F | C | F | R | X | W | S | P | T | B | X | A | U |
| Z | O | F | P | S | Q | D | F | P | A | S | W | F | S | D |
| M | C | K | D | E | K | S | C | P | K | M | K | V | K | R |
| U | P | Z | U | S | P | L | A | N | T | E | R | G | E | U |
| X | O | Z | B | X | P | T | B | I | M | N | Z | A | T | M |
| U | T | U | T | C | J | M | Q | E | D | T | T | E | U | H |

Find the following types of plant container in the grid.

| POT | BOWL | CACHEPOT |
|-----|------|----------|
| TROUGH | PLANTER | BASKET |
| BARREL | SILL | BOX |

# ACROSTICS

Solve the clues correctly and the shaded squares will reveal a vegetable commonly grown in gardens. What is it?

1. Type of sword
2. To remove restraint
3. Indigenous person
4. Symptom or sensation associated with vomiting
5. Fifth prime number

| 1. | | | | | |
|----|----|----|----|----|----|
| 2. | | | | | |
| 3. | | | | | |
| 4. | | | | | |
| 5. | | | | | |

# TRIVIA

All living organisms have scientific names, many of them descriptive and useful in some way or another. Below are three words often found in the scientific names of plants. But do you know what they mean?

### 1. *ANGUSTIFOLIA*
a) Rough bark
b) Narrow leaf
c) Waxy stem

### 2. *PRATENSIS*
a) Relating to a meadow
b) Relating to coastal regions
c) Relating to dense woodland

### 3. *ODORATA*
a) Spiny
b) Variegated
c) Perfumed

# GARDENING WORDS

Gardeners love to get their hands dirty, so here are three words relating to soil and mud. But do you know the meaning of them?

### 1. MARL
a) Clay soil typically comprising 30–65 per cent calcium carbonate
b) Any type of relatively nutrient-rich soil found north of the Arctic Circle
c) Muddy substrate with optimal aeration rates

### 2. FRIABLE
a) Soil that does not become waterlogged
b) Commercially manufactured soil that is available all year round
c) Soil that is easily crumbled

### 3. GLEY
a) Heavy mud usually found in amphibian-rich ponds
b) Poor draining, waterlogged soils with low oxygen levels
c) Muddy soil with unusually high levels of salt and potassium

# SPOT THE DIFFERENCE

Can you spot the five differences between the two pictures?

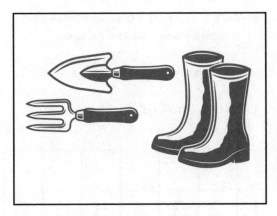

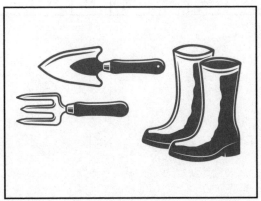

# WORD GROWER

The letters of a seven-letter word have been numbered 1 to 7. Solve the clues to reveal a type of patio feature.

**Letters 6, 2, 3 and 4 give us a body part also known as the collum.**

**Letters 7, 5 and 6 give us a type of spirit.**

**Letters 4, 5 and 1 give us a young goat.**

| | | | | | | |
|---|---|---|---|---|---|---|
| 1 | 2 | 3 | 4 | 5 | 6 | 7 |

# MYSTERY SUDOKU

Complete the grid so that every row, column and 3 × 3 box contains the letters GONWRAMIT in any order. One row or column contains a six-letter word that is a very common practice in gardening.

|   |   |   |   | A |   |   | W |   |
|---|---|---|---|---|---|---|---|---|
|   |   |   |   | W |   |   |   | N |
|   |   | R | T |   |   | M |   |   |
|   | O |   |   | W |   |   | R |   |
| N | W |   |   | G |   |   |   | A |
|   | R | A | N |   |   | W |   |   |
| T |   |   | A | N |   | G |   |   |
|   |   |   | I |   | O |   |   |   |
| A |   | N |   | T |   |   |   |   |

# BETWEEN THE LINES

The name of a flowering plant can be inserted in the blank line so that, reading downwards, eight three-letter words are formed. What is the hidden word between the lines?

| A | C | A | P | A | F | P | C |
|---|---|---|---|---|---|---|---|
|   |   |   |   |   |   |   |   |
| E | T | P | A | E | U | G | P |

# HOW MANY?

How many times does the letter "P" appear on this page?

**Peter Piper picked a peck of pickled peppers.**
**If Peter Piper picked a peck of pickled peppers,**
**how many pecks of pickled peppers did Peter Piper pick?**

# WORD SEARCH: GLOBAL EMBLEMS

| | | | | | | | | | | | | | |
|---|---|---|---|---|---|---|---|---|---|---|---|---|---|
| U | A | G | D | S | C | Y | V | D | T | J | A | R | N | T |
| P | U | G | R | S | F | Q | V | B | S | V | H | L | U | C |
| P | R | Z | I | E | G | M | H | E | T | Q | Q | L | J | M |
| H | Z | O | Y | W | D | J | P | T | J | M | I | G | E | T |
| M | Y | B | T | G | R | N | N | N | P | C | X | P | H |
| B | X | Z | P | E | T | Y | E | I | A | J | C | O | R | I |
| D | Q | W | A | E | A | O | V | V | K | U | X | W | M | S |
| A | N | N | O | F | P | O | N | G | A | Y | E | E | F | T |
| F | I | E | X | B | I | A | V | J | L | L | K | L | O | L |
| F | U | M | Q | S | V | D | V | N | I | M | A | O | M | E |
| O | Y | A | E | D | G | Y | R | M | Y | H | P | T | L | D |
| D | J | L | B | U | S | A | O | F | C | M | J | U | B | C |
| I | N | C | G | E | B | M | B | Q | C | R | O | S | E | L |
| L | H | Y | N | H | A | G | A | G | Q | A | M | X | L | Q |
| S | L | C | O | C | X | U | T | Y | O | G | F | G | K | E |

If you're a globetrotting gardener, this one will particularly appeal to you! Find the following national flowers in the grid.

| THISTLE | DAFFODIL | CYCLAMEN |
|---|---|---|
| CAMOMILE | LAVENDER | PROTEA |
| TULIP | ROSE | LOTUS |

# CROSSWORD: POLLINATION

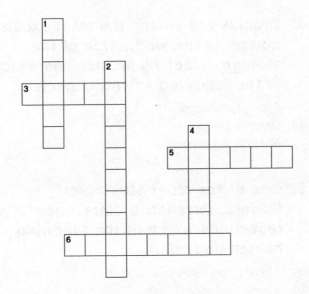

## ACROSS

**3.** A particular kind, type or fashion (5)

**5.** Receives pollen – mark of disgrace? (6)

**6.** Slender part – also found in electric bulbs (8)

## DOWN

**1.** Sounds like a small firearm (6)

**2.** Container (10)

**4.** Male reproductive organ (6)

# TRIVIA: STRANGE BUT TRUE

1. **Orchids are among the most exquisite flowers in the world. One of the strangest-looking orchids has which of the following scientific names?**

a) *Cyclops unicorna*
b) *Dracula vampira*
c) *Medusa leprechauna*

2. **One of the most striking of flowers, *Psychotria elata*, uncannily resembles which of the following human body parts?**

a) A bald head (with age spots!)
b) A nose (with hair!)
c) A pair of lips (with lipstick!)

# PAIRS GAME

Match up the 20 gardening tools in 20 seconds. The first one has been done for you.

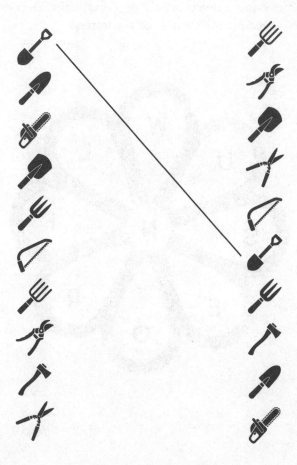

# WORD FLOWER

How many words of four or more letters can you make from the letters below? All words must include the central letter, and proper nouns don't count! Also, can you find the name of a much-loved plant that uses all the letters?

# MAZE

Can you get through this hedge maze from top to bottom in under 30 seconds?

# ANAGRAMS: TREE SHAPES

Rearrange these letters to reveal words used by gardeners to describe shapes of trees.

## LACONIC

## DEAD HOUN DER

## DUNP USE LO

# WORD LADDER

In this word ladder, change one letter at a time to turn the word "doer" into a word that most plants have: "root".

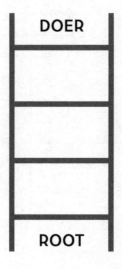

DOER

ROOT

# CROSSWORD: SPORTS PLAYED ON A FRESHLY MOWN LAWN

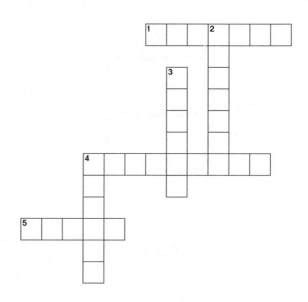

## ACROSS

**1.** Leather on willow (7)

**4.** Requires a net and feathered projectile (9)

**5.** Hit the jack (5)

## DOWN

**2.** Go through hoops (7)

**3.** Anyone for this racquet sport? (6)

**4.** Popular in France (6)

# COUNTING CONUNDRUM

🔨 + 🔨 + 🔨 = 30

🔨 + ✂️ + ✂️ = 20

✂️ + 🍴 + 🍴 = 9

✂️ + ( 🍴 × ✂️ ) = ?

# DOWN THE MIDDLE

Complete all the following words correctly to reveal, in the shaded squares, a place you love to be.

| E | D |  | E | R |
| S | N |  | I | L |
| S | P |  | A | Y |
| H | E |  | G | E |
| S | H |  | D | S |
| P | O |  | D | S |

# WORD SEARCH: IN THE ALLOTMENT

```
S H G A A H A G H G T R L D G
J H C H E R V I R D E I Y T B
H U E A N B A Y L A S G T A D
P A R D L E Y P G A V J U R G
V C G R E E N H O U S E D R N
A S Y H B O J A N B V C L A I
N E I G H B O U R S D X P G G
H T F C D E T K V C T Y H C G
I T M A R J A R A M E N M O I
F X S A F E D V A N R B U M D
B F G P R T E A F M I N B P R
W P H B T K G F E N F E L O J
M K A L M H B V R E N A R S H
V E T Y T I N U M M O C O T K
T E A B R F D R O S B M A R Y
```

Find the following words associated with allotments in the grid.

| | | |
|---|---|---|
| SHED | COMPOST | GRAVEL |
| GREENHOUSE | DIGGING | NEIGHBOURS |
| BONFIRE | COMMUNITY | TEA BREAK |

# ACROSTICS

Solve the clues correctly and the letters in the shaded squares will reveal a word associated with both plants and composts. What is it?

1. Originating from a distant/foreign country
2. Gambling competition involving tickets
3. Colour between blue and violet
4. Throat lozenge
5. Calculating tool known as a "counting frame"

| 1. | | | | | |
|----|--|--|--|--|--|
| 2. | | | | | |
| 3. | | | | | |
| 4. | | | | | |
| 5. | | | | | |

# TRIVIA

1. **The world's most northerly botanical garden is located in which country?**

   a) China
   b) Canada
   c) Norway

2. **In 2018, the world's tallest supported topiary structure was built using more than 1,000 different flowers. On whom was the impressive floral design based?**

   a) Queen Elizabeth II
   b) Mickey Mouse
   c) Elvis Presley

3. **In November 2016, 286 people gathered in Kuwait to take part in what event?**

   a) The world's largest potato-tasting session
   b) The world's largest gardening lesson
   c) The world's largest digital horticultural seminar

# GARDENING WORDS

Test your gardening knowledge with these three words relating to specific parts of plants. There are two red herrings for each word – can you pick the correct definition?

### 1. ACAULOUS
a) Semi-succulent stem
b) Without a stem or without a visible stem
c) Stem that is at least 50 per cent covered in thorns or prickles

### 2. ACICULA
a) A needle-like prickle
b) The smallest type of node
c) The thinnest kind of stem

### 3. BRACT
a) A root in an early stage of fungal infection
b) A dead or inactive flower, often found in arid conditions
c) A modified leaf, often mistaken for the flower

# SPOT THE DIFFERENCE

Can you spot the five differences between the two pictures?

# WORD GROWER

The letters of a nine-letter word have been numbered 1 to 9. Solve the clues to reveal a common shrub.

**Letters 2, 8, 5 and 4 give us a name for 12 months.**

**Letters 1, 9, 6 and 3 give us a unit of measurement.**

**Letters 4, 9 and 7 give us a word for tattered material.**

| | | | | | | | | |
|---|---|---|---|---|---|---|---|---|
| 1 | 2 | 3 | 4 | 5 | 6 | 7 | 8 | 9 |

# MYSTERY SUDOKU

Complete the grid so that every row, column and 3 × 3 box contains the letters TRAGWINES in any order. One row or column contains an eight-letter word that is a crucial job for most gardeners.

| | | | G | | | | A | |
| --- | --- | --- | --- | --- | --- | --- | --- | --- |
| | A | T | | | | | | |
| | | R | | | S | N | | T |
| | G | | N | | | | R | A |
| | W | | | | | I | | |
| | T | | A | | | | S | E |
| | | I | | | T | E | | N |
| | S | W | | | | | | |
| | | | W | | | | T | |

# BETWEEN
# THE LINES

A word used to describe plants that thrive in adverse conditions can be inserted in the blank line so that, reading downwards, nine three-letter words are formed. What is the hidden word between the lines?

| T | J | I | O | P | O | N | A | A |
|---|---|---|---|---|---|---|---|---|
|   |   |   |   |   |   |   |   |   |
| Y | R | E | E | T | E | T | S | P |

# CROSS OUT

Cross out all the letters that appear more than once. The letters that are left, reading from left to right and top to bottom, will spell out something that grows in a garden. What is it?

| T | F | A | S | Y | I | H | P |
|---|---|---|---|---|---|---|---|
| A | C | L | K | U | U | B | S |
| O | T | B | D | W | E | D | A |
| Y | P | I | S | C | K | R | H |

# WORD SEARCH: EXOTIC PLANTS

| | | | | | | | | | | | | | | |
|---|---|---|---|---|---|---|---|---|---|---|---|---|---|---|
| L | E | H | L | R | B | F | P | J | E | I | Y | D | K | I |
| K | N | A | P | I | G | N | A | R | F | C | P | Q | R | K |
| B | O | U | G | A | I | N | V | I | L | L | E | A | A | S |
| I | Q | Q | O | Y | P | W | G | W | C | D | D | W | U | U |
| N | E | G | T | J | A | S | M | I | N | E | K | R | O | H |
| D | H | U | P | R | Y | Q | L | H | M | O | O | Y | W | T |
| N | J | A | J | T | I | V | K | P | S | B | Q | X | D | N |
| K | V | F | G | A | I | U | J | A | E | Z | D | I | E | A |
| U | Q | Q | D | A | B | K | R | L | V | F | X | S | Y | P |
| N | O | D | L | Q | V | J | L | M | T | M | L | Q | M | A |
| D | T | H | C | T | Y | E | J | L | V | R | Z | G | L | G |
| T | M | F | P | A | H | U | I | V | C | E | U | R | Z | A |
| R | W | S | Y | X | V | C | N | U | T | L | O | F | K | X |
| I | V | Q | U | N | F | X | R | G | C | O | I | L | R | Z |
| X | C | O | R | D | Y | L | I | N | E | A | Z | X | A | X |

Dream about sunnier climes by finding the
following exotic plants in the grid.

| | | |
|---|---|---|
| **ALOE** | **JASMINE** | **HELLEBORUS** |
| **CORDYLINE** | **PALM** | **AGAPANTHUS** |
| **BOUGAINVILLEA** | **FRANGIPAN** | **AGAVE** |

# CROSSWORD: TRADITIONAL MEANINGS OF FLOWER COLOURS

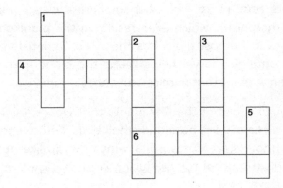

The colour symbolizes...

## ACROSS

**4.** Royalty and success (6)

**6.** Excitement, fervour, enthusiasm (6)

## DOWN

**1.** Tranquillity and peace (4)

**2.** Happiness, friendship and joy (6)

**3.** Rebirth and renewal (5)

**5.** True love and passion (3)

# TRIVIA

*Boquila trifoliolata* is a fruit-bearing plant native to Chile and Argentina. That's not so unusual, right? However, the plant *is* unusual – some would say creepy. Why?

a) It grows vines, which can change shape according to its host plant. The phenomenon is called "mimetic polymorphism", which even results in the plant growing spines if the host plant has them too. Scientists believe this strange marvel helps keeps the plant from being eaten. A plant that mimics other ones – surely not!

b) *Boquila* is one of the few plants that waves its vines in the air to attract bats and small birds, before engulfing the hapless creatures in its Venus flytrap-like opening. It's also unusual for producing acid to digest its prey. Whatever next?

c) The South American plant is notorious as the plant that has caused the most human deaths. This is due to its sinister ability to unwittingly wrap its vines around walkers, resulting in injury and, in some cases, accidental death. It sounds like something from a horror film!

# PAIRS GAME

Match up the 20 trees in 20 seconds. The first one has been done for you.

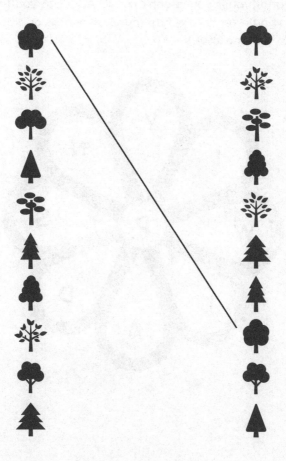

# WORD FLOWER

See how many words of four or more letters you can make from the letters below. All words must include the central letter, and proper nouns don't count! Also, can you find the name of a flower (two words, found on heaths and uplands) that uses all the letters?

# MAZE

Can you get through this hedge maze from top to bottom in under 30 seconds?

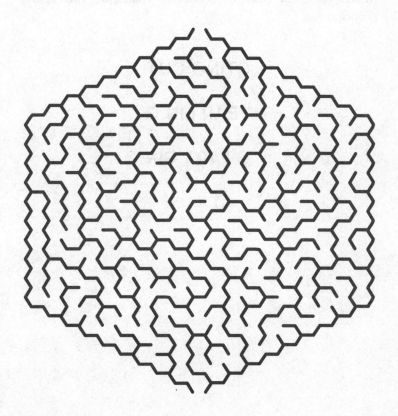

# ANAGRAMS: PROPAGATION

Rearrange these letters to reveal words associated with plant propagation.

### STING CUT

### YEAR LIN G

### G FART GIN

# WORD LADDER

Gardening forks are sold in their millions all over the world. In this word ladder, change one letter at a time to turn the word "sold" into "fork".

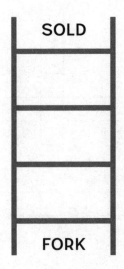

SOLD

FORK

# CROSSWORD: A MIXED BUNCH

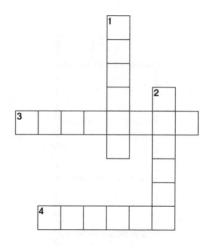

## ACROSS

**3.** Film title and off-white colour (8)

**4.** *Capsicum* (6)

## DOWN

**1.** Prone to weeping (6)

**2.** Redhead, Rogers (6)

# COUNTING CONUNDRUM

🦋 × 🐜 = 72

🐜 × 🐌 = 36

🦋 × 🐌 = 32

🦋 = ?    🐜 = ?    🐌 = ?

# RIDDLES

1. I am a seed with three letters in my name. Take away the last two and I still sound the same. What am I?

2. What has eyes but cannot see?

# WORD SEARCH: CLIMBERS

```
J  F  R  C  B  I  W  N  V  F  W  D  W  Y  J
X  H  M  E  Q  J  O  P  D  D  C  A  J  Z  D
K  D  O  R  C  B  N  L  T  A  I  O  D  Q  R
H  T  K  N  O  D  Z  H  T  R  M  C  B  L  E
Z  L  A  I  E  J  E  U  E  W  V  I  T  E  P
B  E  D  U  Y  Y  T  T  X  Z  E  J  R  I  E
T  A  E  C  V  O  S  F  T  S  K  W  X  A  E
Y  D  Y  I  A  I  I  U  O  I  R  R  C  I  R
L  W  S  R  W  Q  N  C  C  M  R  H  L  B  C
B  O  F  D  X  K  Q  E  P  K  Z  R  E  I  I
K  R  K  O  L  P  I  M  U  R  L  D  M  Z  F
G  T  Q  H  G  D  D  X  B  B  B  E  A  K  X
D  C  X  Q  N  P  L  M  X  K  S  H  T  W  J
S  O  L  A  N  U  M  E  M  K  R  M  I  U  G
Q  F  R  E  W  O  L  F  N  O  I  S  S  A  P
```

Find the following climbing plants in the grid.

| | | |
|---|---|---|
| **HONEYSUCKLE** | **LEADWORT** | **WISTERIA** |
| **IVY** | **VINE** | **SOLANUM** |
| **CLEMATIS** | **PASSIONFLOWER** | **CREEPER** |

# ACROSTICS

Solve the clues correctly and the shaded squares will reveal a plant often seen in Western films. What is it?

1. Halt an opponent in sport
2. Warm temperatures will undo the chill.
3. Optical phenomenon
4. Central American country
5. Reptile

| 1. | | | | | |
|----|--|--|--|--|--|
| 2. | | | | | |
| 3. | | | | | |
| 4. | | | | | |
| 5. | | | | | |

# TRIVIA

The Hampton Court Flower Show in London is the world's largest flower show and an annual highlight for gardeners everywhere. Which three of the following five statements are true?

a) It was first held in 1970

b) It stretches over 34 acres

c) Special trains were laid on for the first shows, going from Waterloo station

d) It attracts an average of 1.5 million visitors per show

e) It takes 200 people to build and dismantle the show

# GARDENING WORDS

Here are three random – but tricky – words relating to gardening. Do you have the knowledge to pick the correct definitions?

### 1. FIMBRIATED
a) Frilly, fringed or jagged, often applies to leaves
b) Highly colourful, often applies to orchids
c) Highly stunted in growth

### 2. PEDICEL
a) A "foot-like" growth on fungi
b) A small stalk or stem
c) A type of acorn

### 3. ALLIUM
a) A word used to describe trees found in peaty soils
b) A small, sac-like growth, often found on aquatic plants
c) A genus comprising onions

# SPOT THE
# DIFFERENCE

Can you spot the five differences between the two pictures?

# WORD GROWER

The letters of an eight-letter word have been numbered 1 to 8. Solve the clues to reveal a word relating to soil.

**Letters 3, 1, 2 and 8 give us a curly vegetable.**

**Letters 5, 4, 3 and 8 give us a body of water.**

**Letters 3, 6 and 7 give us another word for "family".**

| | | | | | | | |
|---|---|---|---|---|---|---|---|
| 1 | 2 | 3 | 4 | 5 | 6 | 7 | 8 |

# MYSTERY SUDOKU

Complete the grid so that every row, column and 3 × 3 box contains the letters TILNUGHSO in any order. One row or column contains an eight-letter word that is something essential for gardening.

| | | N | S | | | | | |
|---|---|---|---|---|---|---|---|---|
| | | I | L | U | | T | | G |
| L | T | | | N | | S | | I |
| | N | | | | | | I | |
| G | L | U | | | | | T | |
| | | | | N | | | | |
| | I | G | | | | | L | |
| | | | I | T | | O | | |
| | U | H | | | | | | S |

# BETWEEN THE LINES

The name of a group of cone-bearing plants can be inserted in the blank line so that, reading downwards, seven three-letter words are formed. What is the hidden word between the lines?

| I | L | A | S | O | S | A |
|---|---|---|---|---|---|---|
|   |   |   |   |   |   |   |
| E | P | T | P | F | T | E |

# HIDDEN FLOWERS

In each of the sentences below, a flower is hidden. For instance, in the sentence "The true maestro serves the music", the word "rose" is hidden in "maest**ro se**rves".

1. Trying to avoid exposure to all the propaganda is your best bet.

2. The concept of energy, or chi, derives from ancient Chinese philosophy.

3. At the Plaza, leather sofas lined the walls of the lobby.

4. Underneath the surface of the lagoon, the croc used all its guile to hunt its prey.

5. During the summer holidays, I go to bed very late and I rise around noon.

# WORD SEARCH: LATIN NAMES

```
L M N V O L T Z A S H P B I E
M A J D W M M X J Y A H R S U
T N V H C I K B E P I U C D P
L Q Q A L T R Z L Q L K G E H
A B W R T I F O D Z O R K I O
V W A Q E E F H D T N M E E R
A P I L U T R K U X G D G G B
T T M F S L S A B S A U K S I
E A S C V S N A H G M L O Q A
R W J T U T Z L E L R M G C J
A I C E H C I X L N S D G F G
D Z R E H V V C U O O F B A V
C D M Q M P X R C D L T G R U
E I Y R Q C B U B C P D O J F
S Z N M T F S A L V I A A C V
```

Find the following plant species or genera in the grid.

BUDDLEJA          LAVATERA          TULIPA

COSMOS          EUPHORBIA          COTONEASTER

SALVIA          ANTHEMIS          MAGNOLIA

# CROSSWORD: GARDEN CRITTERS

## ACROSS

**3.** Commonly found in soil, eats organic matter (9)

**4.** Larval stage in butterfly's life cycle (11)

**6.** Daddy longlegs (5, 3)

## DOWN

**1.** Eight-legged arthropod (6)

**2.** Segmented with varying numbers of legs (9)

**5.** Shell-less gastropod (4)

123

# TRIVIA

Identify the correct statement from this short list – the rest are red herrings. It's a beauty of a fact!

a) Certain species of heather were highly desirable and were given to Queen Victoria as birthday presents because they produced gold-coloured dust

b) Prior to the twentieth century, reptile excrement was used for fertilizer, and proved so effective that it was bagged and sold to some of the most famous gardeners, including Lancelot "Capability" Brown

c) The *Gregaria* genus of plants are the only type that reduce in length the more they grow

d) Technically, sunflowers are not just one flower. Both the brown centre and the classic yellow petals are collectively over 1,000 individual flowers

e) Antartica is the only continent to have no native flowering plant species

# PAIRS GAME

Match up the 20 insects in 20 seconds. The first one has been done for you.

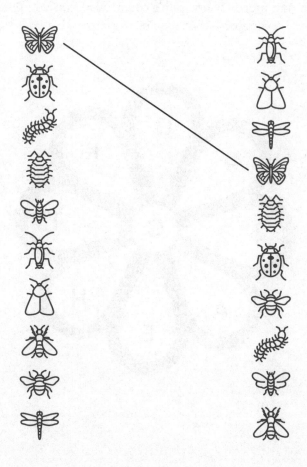

# WORD FLOWER

See how many words of four or more letters you can make from the letters below. All words must include the central letter, and proper nouns don't count! Also, can you find the name of a vegetable that uses all the letters?

# MAZE

Can you get from the bottom to the middle of this hedge maze in under 30 seconds?

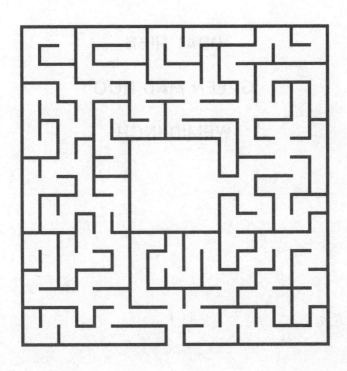

# ANAGRAMS: ORNAMENTS

Rearrange these letters to reveal types of ornaments commonly found in gardens.

### DRAT HIBB

### GREEN MAD NOG

### WEMID INCH

# WORD LADDER

In this word ladder, change one letter at a time to turn the word "ping" into a favourite citrus tree: "lime".

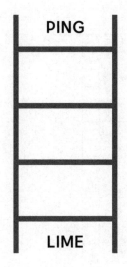

PING

LIME

# CROSSWORD: TREE SAMPLE

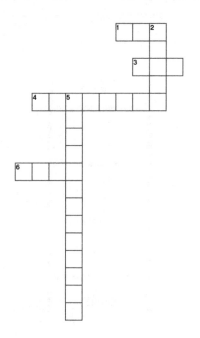

## ACROSS

**1.** Remnants of a fire (3)

**3.** Nightmare on this street (3)

**4.** Favourable wood for making furniture (8)

**6.** Common conifer yielding cones (4)

## DOWN

**2.** Spiny festive plant (5)

**5.** Equine plus thorax plus kernel, e.g. acorn (5, 8)

# COUNTING
# CONUNDRUM

🥾 + 🥾 + 🥾 = 12

( 🥾 × 🥾 ) + 🧤 = 26

🧤 + ( 🧤 × ✂️ ) = 100

🧤 + ( ✂️ × 🥾 ) = ?

# WORD LINK

Each of the three words in the clues below have a word in common. For example, if the clues were "count", "faith" and "weight", the answer would be "lose" (lose count, lose faith and lose weight). Answer each of the following clues correctly to reveal a word in the shaded column, which is a type of flower.

1. fee, riser, night

2. clearance, dog, dweller

3. leader, following, film

4. road, bad, wire

5. up, dream, water

| 1. | | | |
|---|---|---|---|
| 2. | | | |
| 3. | | | |
| 4. | | | |
| 5. | | | |

# WORD SEARCH: AQUATIC PLANTS

```
T  H  G  A  A  H  A  V  H  G  T  R  L  D  G
Q  R  P  D  E  E  W  D  N  O  P  G  R  D  A
H  T  B  V  C  G  A  A  V  V  O  G  G  T  W
I  R  S  E  K  I  N  G  C  U  P  S  O  S  Z
B  O  M  B  G  U  C  L  Y  B  Y  N  L  G  W
O  W  X  U  K  M  P  I  S  X  L  Q  D  Z  A
F  R  A  F  H  M  W  U  W  G  S  R  E  X  T
W  A  T  E  R  P  L  A  N  T  A  I  N  P  E
D  T  C  Q  T  O  Y  T  V  D  S  G  C  E  R
X  S  V  S  V  F  G  U  E  D  J  M  L  K  L
A  B  N  M  H  M  N  B  Z  G  L  S  U  W  I
J  I  N  Z  V  P  L  N  I  D  Z  F  B  N  L
Q  O  C  O  G  L  Q  T  N  T  D  R  D  I  Y
G  T  M  U  R  A  G  O  B  S  U  S  B  N  C
S  K  U  N  K  C  A  B  B  A  G  E  P  G  Y
```

Find the following water plants in the grid.

| | | |
|---|---|---|
| **WATER PLANTAIN** | **FROGBIT** | **GOLDEN CLUB** |
| **PONDWEED** | **WATER LILY** | **BOG ARUM** |
| **STARWORT** | **SKUNK CABBAGE** | **KINGCUP** |

# ACROSTICS

Solve the clues correctly and the shaded squares will reveal a common flower. What is it?

1. Female sibling
2. Interstellar clouds
3. Vehicle safety feature
4. Human-powered watercraft
5. Edible fruit similar to plums

| 1. | | | | | |
|----|---|---|---|---|---|
| 2. | | | | | |
| 3. | | | | | |
| 4. | | | | | |
| 5. | | | | | |

# TRIVIA

An orchestra with a bizarre horticultural twist was founded in Vienna in 1998. The name of the musical group would give the question away, so have a stab at why the orchestra is so unique.

a) The musicians all have first and last names that are shared with flowers

b) The musicians all perform on instruments made out of vegetables

c) Eschewing concert halls, the orchestra performs entirely in gardens around the world

d) They are the only orchestra to have government permission to perform under the influence of marijuana

# GARDENING WORDS

The gardening world is full of wonderful words, but do you know the meaning of the following?

### 1. ANTHOCYANIN
a) A type of rainbow that stimulates plant growth
b) A plant pigment
c) A species of fungus

### 2. AUGER
a) A gardening tool to take soil samples or make holes
b) A type of slate commonly used in patio construction
c) A feature of alpine rockeries

### 3. BIPINNATE
a) A plant with two main sections
b) A leaf structure
c) A family of earth-dwelling crustaceans

# SPOT THE
# DIFFERENCE

Can you spot the five differences between the two pictures?

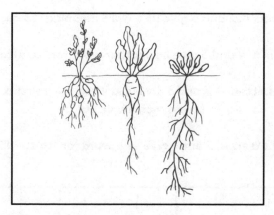

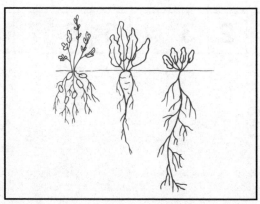

# WORD GROWER

The letters of an eight-letter word have been numbered 1 to 8. Solve the clues to reveal a common fungal plant disease.

**Letters 4, 2 and 6 give us a word meaning "to decay".**

**Letters 6, 4 and 5 give us another word for "to attempt".**

**Letters 8, 7 and 3 give us a word for "to relax on a bench, chair, etc."**

**Letters 4, 2 and 1 give us a word for "to steal".**

| 1 | 2 | 3 | 4 | 5 | 6 | 7 | 8 |

# MYSTERY SUDOKU

Complete the grid so that every row, column and 3 × 3 box contains the letters MURIGONAC in any order. One row or column contains a seven-letter word that is a type of gardening.

| | | | | | N | | | |
|---|---|---|---|---|---|---|---|---|
| | | I | A | | | | | M |
| | | | | I | | | O | C |
| | C | | | G | O | | | I |
| A | U | | | | | | G | N |
| M | | G | R | | | C | | |
| N | R | | | C | | | | |
| O | | | | U | M | | | |
| | | M | | | | | | |

# BETWEEN
# THE LINES

Something that all plants need can be inserted in the blank line so that, reading downwards, nine three-letter words are formed. What is the hidden word between the lines?

| I | B | A | O | D | P | E | S | A |
|---|---|---|---|---|---|---|---|---|
|   |   |   |   |   |   |   |   |   |
| K | S | E | E | G | N | D | Y | K |

# MISSING PLANT

Insert the name of a plant so that, reading downwards, five five-letter words are formed. What is the plant?

| S | C | T | L | C |
|---|---|---|---|---|
| U | R | R | I | O |
|   |   |   |   |   |
| E | S | L | E | L |
| R | T | L | N | Y |

# WORD SEARCH: BEAUTIFUL LANDSCAPES

```
K  H  G  A  A  H  A  V  H  G  T  R  L  D  G
S  Z  Z  T  S  I  Y  Q  F  P  A  T  I  O  X
Q  P  K  R  C  I  K  U  D  O  J  O  F  P  R
N  J  P  E  R  G  O  L  A  Z  R  D  D  I  W
I  W  V  L  E  P  H  M  G  H  W  Y  Y  M  Y
E  X  W  L  C  Y  E  A  X  S  I  M  O  V  D
K  K  Y  I  S  Z  L  J  D  E  Q  H  X  O  B
G  A  B  S  A  L  G  E  N  P  X  S  L  F  P
I  G  V  X  Z  E  B  A  Y  W  Q  Y  S  P  A
Y  W  D  W  K  R  A  Q  V  M  A  P  E  L  V
E  T  N  I  E  I  N  X  Y  T  E  L  G  C  I
C  I  N  W  X  Y  U  H  C  S  C  Z  L  C  N
N  S  O  J  A  N  J  Y  V  J  P  L  N  E  G
E  L  R  Q  F  L  W  X  D  P  W  Q  S  O  J
F  N  D  P  Z  N  E  D  E  C  K  I  N  G  W
```

Perfect the art of landscape gardening by finding the following words relating to DIY gardening.

| DECKING | FLOWER BED | FENCE |
|---------|-----------|-------|
| LAWN | PERGOLA | WALL |
| PATIO | TRELLIS | PAVING |

# CROSSWORD: IN THE WOODS

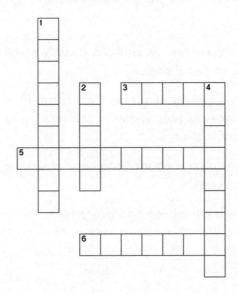

## ACROSS

**3.** Thicket, grove, small group of trees (5)

**5.** Bird that taps on tree trunks (10)

**6.** Prickly shrub (7)

## DOWN

**1.** Amphibian sits on this (9)

**2.** Clearing, open area (5)

**4.** Tree with foliage all year round (9)

# TRIVIA

Soil can be critical for the success of your plants. It's a mostly innocuous material, but it can be fascinating nonetheless (no, really). Which one of the following statements relating to soil is correct?

a) Pound for pound, Greenpeace considers soil the most valuable material on Earth

b) Most soils in Australia more than 15 cm (6 in.) beneath the surface are purple, due to minerals being deposited millions of years ago

c) People who have an irrational fear of soil are known as "loamophobes"

d) Typically, there are more microorganisms in one teaspoon (5 grams) of soil than there are people on Earth

# PAIRS GAME

Match up the 20 vegetables in 20 seconds. The first one has been done for you.

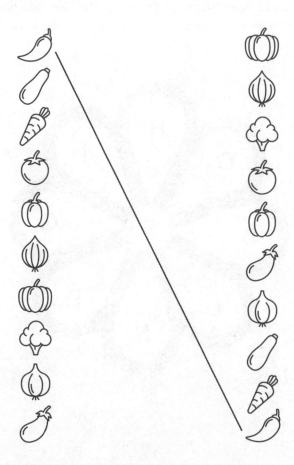

# WORD FLOWER

See how many words of four or more letters you can make from the letters below. All words must include the central letter, and proper nouns don't count! Also, can you find the name of a common garden bird that uses all the letters?

# MAZE

Can you get through this hedge maze from top to bottom in under 30 seconds?

# ANAGRAMS: SOMETHING SHRUBBERY

Rearrange these letters to reveal types of shrub shape.

ECTER

NUDRO

SPRING EAD

# WORD LADDER

In this word ladder, change one letter at a time to turn the word "boar" into "peat" – a common substrate used by gardeners.

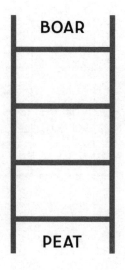

BOAR

PEAT

# CROSSWORD: PHOTOSYNTHESIS WORDS

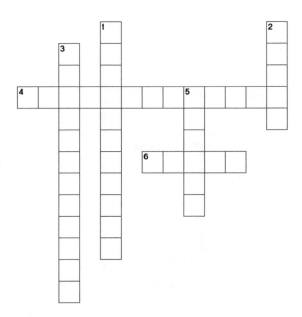

## ACROSS

**4.** Gas absorbed from air by plants (6, 7)

**6.** Plants convert this energy into chemical energy (5)

## DOWN

**1.** Green pigment (11)

**2.** Essential liquid (5)

**3.** E.g. sugar, starch (12)

**5.** Gaseous waste product (6)

# COUNTING CONUNDRUM

$$\text{chainsaw} + \text{chainsaw} + \text{chainsaw} + \text{chainsaw} = 80$$

$$\text{chainsaw} + (\text{saw} + \text{saw}) = 84$$

$$\text{axe axe} - \text{saw} = 10$$

$$\text{chainsaw} + (\text{axe} \times \text{saw}) = \text{?}$$

# MINI SUDOKU: WINTER

Winter is a time for gardeners to slow down, plan and prepare for the year ahead. Here's a chance to enjoy winter in another way by completing the grid so that every row, column and 2 × 3 box contains the letters that make up the word "winter".

|   | I |   |   |   |
|---|---|---|---|---|---|
| W |   |   |   | I |
| N |   |   | E |   |
|   | W |   |   |   |
|   |   | T |   |   |
| E |   | W |   | R |

# WORD SEARCH: THE LAND OF GIANTS

| | | | | | | | | | | | | | |
|---|---|---|---|---|---|---|---|---|---|---|---|---|---|
| S | U | R | P | Y | C | A | J | M | S | S | U | Q | Q | R |
| R | N | F | X | K | I | P | N | O | J | T | O | C | L | T |
| T | C | B | I | O | T | D | N | U | C | K | T | Y | I | P |
| G | Q | G | U | H | W | H | C | N | D | R | A | S | G | F |
| P | U | Q | V | S | M | Z | U | T | K | V | T | U | G | M |
| V | E | J | Z | P | D | I | N | A | B | V | F | O | R | U |
| S | F | N | R | A | S | N | H | I | I | H | R | K | D | I |
| U | R | X | E | M | C | H | B | N | V | J | D | U | E | K |
| G | V | V | D | O | U | G | L | A | S | F | I | R | C | P |
| A | M | V | W | Z | T | K | K | S | L | W | J | X | V | K |
| R | A | T | O | R | O | Z | D | H | B | O | H | B | A | U |
| P | A | Q | O | Q | W | K | H | I | O | S | N | T | P | B |
| I | C | P | D | G | M | A | N | N | A | G | U | M | A | V |
| N | C | Y | T | U | W | Z | O | M | W | T | P | N | O | G |
| E | T | Z | O | S | U | T | P | Y | L | A | C | U | E | Y |

Find the following trees in the grid – most of them are among the world's tallest.

REDWOOD          DOUGLAS FIR          CYPRUS

SEQUOIA          MOUNTAIN ASH          KAURI

SUGAR PINE          MANNA GUM          EUCALYPTUS

# ACROSTICS

Solve the clues correctly and the shaded squares will reveal a variety of pear. What is it?

1. Fourth sign of the zodiac
2. Citrus fruit
3. Serviette
4. Material
5. Safe to eat

| 1. | | | | | |
|----|----|----|----|----|----|
| 2. | | | | | |
| 3. | | | | | |
| 4. | | | | | |
| 5. | | | | | |

# TRIVIA

In 2021, it was reported that the oldest tree in the eastern USA could be under threat due to rising sea levels. Bald cypress trees are native to the south-eastern USA and this particular one has been towering over waters in North Carolina's Black River for some time. But what age is this botanical stalwart?

a) 1,368 years

b) 2,624 years

c) 3,897 years

d) 5,109 years

# GARDENING WORDS

It's time to test your horticultural knowledge with another trio of devilish words. Can you find the correct definitions?

### 1. THATCH
a) Smooth rock formation often found when digging pathways
b) Layer of material near the soil surface that hasn't decomposed
c) Dense mud formed at the bottom of algae-rich ponds

### 2. CORM
a) Alternative name for blackberries
b) An underground storage system found in certain plants
c) Popular type of bird seed, especially in North America

### 3. CLEISTOGAMOUS
a) Carnivorous plants, e.g. Venus flytrap
b) Another word for variegated flowers
c) Self-fertile flowers that don't open

156

# SPOT THE DIFFERENCE

Can you spot the five differences between the two pictures?

# WORD GROWER

The letters of a ten-letter word have been numbered 1 to 10. Solve the clues to reveal a structure commonly found in gardens.

**Letters 6, 3 and 5 give us a female chicken.**

**Letters 8, 9 and 4 give us another word for "to utilize".**

**Letters 1, 7, 2 and 10 give us the surname of a former US vice-president.**

| 1 | 2 | 3 | 4 | 5 | 6 | 7 | 8 | 9 | 10 |

# MYSTERY SUDOKU

Complete the grid so that every row, column and 3 × 3 box contains the letters DULCEPARO in any order. One row or column contains a seven-letter word that is the tasty end result of certain kinds of gardening.

| P |   | O | D |   |   |   |   | L |
|   | C |   | L |   |   | R |   | O |
|   |   |   | R |   |   | U |   |   |
|   |   |   | L | D |   |   |   |   |
|   |   | D |   |   | U |   | P |   |
|   |   |   | A | C |   |   |   |   |
|   |   |   | U |   |   | P |   |   |
| A |   | P |   |   |   | O |   | R |
| R |   | U | O |   |   |   |   | A |

# BETWEEN THE LINES

A well-known genus of common plants can be inserted in the blank line so that, reading downwards, eight three-letter words are formed. What is the hidden plant genus between the lines?

| A | T | O | M | A | R | R | E |
|---|---|---|---|---|---|---|---|
|   |   |   |   |   |   |   |   |
| E | N | C | P | D | G | G | U |

# HOW MANY?

How many times does the letter "O" appear on this page?

**Do you know your onions? The origin of this phrase is the subject of debate, but it basically means to be knowledgeable about something.**

# WORD SEARCH: IN THE GARDEN

| K | H | D | F | A | U | O | G | V | S | E | E | R | O | G |
| E | L | I | S | Y | S | R | I | M | T | U | B | S | D | N |
| C | O | L | P | Z | Z | T | M | A | L | A | M | D | Y | I |
| C | U | T | T | I | N | G | N | U | K | M | M | U | R | S |
| Q | F | F | N | B | N | I | K | P | I | T | F | T | H | S |
| M | P | J | S | B | M | I | E | U | K | H | O | T | A | E |
| N | W | X | I | R | I | R | W | T | H | I | J | D | N | R |
| O | M | V | E | A | E | E | F | V | D | Y | F | B | A | D |
| G | Y | G | S | N | A | W | N | S | K | U | W | V | E | P |
| F | K | X | N | L | G | A | X | N | U | P | H | B | R | O |
| E | T | I | L | H | J | M | K | E | I | E | N | O | O | T |
| X | A | V | T | N | A | L | P | S | N | A | R | T | B | I |
| L | V | Q | X | M | P | L | J | N | B | G | L | Y | I | O |
| X | D | R | C | S | X | H | E | M | K | S | B | T | C | A |
| C | R | H | I | Z | O | M | E | E | X | D | H | A | L | S |

Find the following gardening terms in the below grid. Some of them might even be new words to you.

| RHIZOME | HUMUS | CUTTING |
| PERENNIAL | TOPDRESSING | BIENNIAL |
| TRANSPLANT | GERMINATE | ANAEROBIC |

# CROSSWORD: SAYING IT WITH FLOWERS

Solve the following clues to reveal flowers commonly given as gifts.

## ACROSS

**3.** Popular flower, name means "water vessel" (9)

**5.** Tropical flower, also known as "Rose of Sharon" (8)

**6.** Famous in Holland (5)

## DOWN

**1.** Old-fashioned milk brand (9)

**2.** Useful for doing the dishes (singular) (8)

**4.** Most romantic of flowers? (4)

# TRIVIA

In 2021, it was reported that a substance helped boost bees' focus and encouraged them to visit scented flowers more quickly. But what on earth is this bee-friendly substance?

a) Concentrated glucose

b) Caffeine

c) Alcohol

d) Nicotine

# PAIRS GAME

Match up the 20 garden gates in 20 seconds. The first one has been done for you.

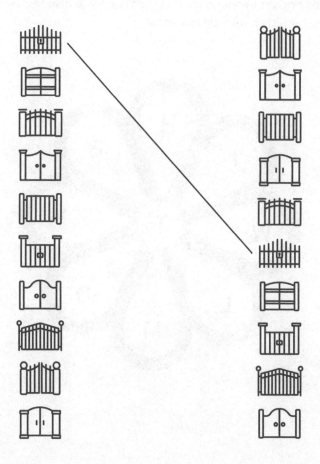

# WORD FLOWER

See how many words of four or more letters you can make from the letters below. All words must include the central letter, and proper nouns don't count! Can you also find a two-word herb that uses all the letters?

# MAZE

Can you get from the top to the middle of this hedge maze in under 30 seconds?

# ANAGRAMS: FEMALE NAMES

Rearrange these letters to reveal plants or flowers that share their name with a female first name.

## HAD PEN

## I RACE

## MORE RIPS

# WORD LADDER

If you can conquer this word ladder you deserve a round of applause! Change one letter at a time to turn the word "clap" into "plum".

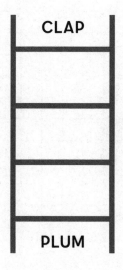

CLAP

PLUM

# CROSSWORD: FLAVOURSOME PLANTS

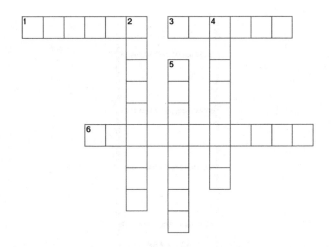

## ACROSS

1. Herb with aniseed flavour (6)
3. Hinders fresh breath (6)
6. Pungent, goes with beef (11)

## DOWN

2. Aromatic flavour, commonly used in confectionery (9)
4. Perfect with lamb (8)
5. Used in liquors and in cake decorations (8)

# COUNTING CONUNDRUM

$$\text{🧹} + \text{🧹} + \text{🧹} = 27$$

$$\text{🧹} - \text{🍴} - \text{🍴} = 3$$

$$\text{🍴} \times \text{🍁} = 6$$

$$\text{🧹} - (\text{🍴} + \text{🍁}) + 1 = ?$$

# RIDDLES

1. What's the first thing a gardener plants in their garden?

2. My hard shell comes in many colours. I prefer to live underground and, when I'm there, if I'm warm and hydrated, I stretch my arms and legs out.

# WORD SEARCH: IN THE RED

```
H  P  L  Q  C  J  S  U  K  V  I  M  K  J  Y
V  E  M  Z  X  I  C  D  I  A  N  T  H  U  S
C  N  E  J  D  Q  O  Q  K  Y  N  Q  W  Q  R
Z  T  T  M  Y  V  A  S  B  N  J  V  O  V  A
R  A  T  L  H  N  W  M  A  K  B  T  H  D  H
A  S  M  T  U  E  O  I  P  T  T  O  Y  S  R
Q  R  X  H  F  C  M  E  K  E  A  W  A  Z  N
S  C  G  Q  S  G  C  Z  P  E  A  D  C  H  G
U  H  P  K  N  E  E  A  D  I  L  O  I  U  T
P  H  C  T  T  O  R  K  N  Q  S  Z  N  C  L
G  O  E  Q  S  E  T  N  W  U  D  Y  T  L  E
C  X  P  T  Y  U  I  R  G  A  I  L  H  A  D
K  S  I  P  G  Z  V  Z  M  D  V  I  G  Z  F
H  P  L  R  Y  A  S  C  D  N  N  A  V  K  L
F  H  M  O  R  C  T  A  I  V  L  A  S  C  N
```

In the grid, find the following flowers that have red varieties

| | | |
|---|---|---|
| POPPY | COCKSCOMB | DAHLIA |
| ZINNIA | PENTAS | HYACINTH |
| PEONY | DIANTHUS | SALVIA |

# ACROSTICS

Solve the clues correctly and the shaded squares will reveal a small fruit commonly grown in gardens. What is it?

1. Shortened word for baking soda
2. Famous TV dog
3. Person skilled with bow and arrow
4. New world vulture
5. Renal organ

| 1. | | | | |
|----|----|----|----|----|
| 2. | | | | |
| 3. | | | | |
| 4. | | | | |
| 5. | | | | |

# TRIVIA

Everyone is familiar with the top three athletes receiving gold, silver and bronze medals at the Olympic Games. What is also ubiquitous on the winning podiums is bouquets of flowers being presented to the athletes. However, at the 2020 Tokyo Olympics (which took place in 2021 due to the global pandemic), the bouquets had a particular significance. What was it?

a) The flowers used to create the bouquets were a cultural symbol of endurance and success

b) The flowers were grown by Japan's leading horticulturalist, whose family is a major philanthropist and has improved the lives of thousands of Japanese people

c) The flowers – yellow, green and blue – were grown almost entirely in three areas of Japan which were devastated in the 2011 earthquake and tsunami, thus honouring the lives lost in the tragedy

d) It is the first time that flowers have been used to mark a sporting victory in any Asian country

# GARDENING WORDS

Get your green fingers scratching your head with this trio of definitions! Do you know the meaning of the following?

### 1. PINCHING OUT
a) Remove growing points of plants to encourage bushier growth
b) Spread dead leaf litter to encourage greater soil nutrition
c) Encourage water transportation through plant tissue

### 2. DIOECIOUS
a) Plants that are both succulent and woody
b) Plants that produce both white and black flowers
c) Plants that have male and female flowers on different plants

### 3. ESPALIER
a) A leaf type in the shape of a sword
b) A form of pruning trees and shrubs
c) A wide-brimmed hat often used by gardeners in hot countries

# SPOT THE
# DIFFERENCE

Can you spot the five differences between the two pictures?

# WORD GROWER

The letters of a seven-letter word have been numbered 1 to 7. Solve the clues to reveal an annual bedding plant.

**Letters 5, 4, 7 and 3 give us a fabric joint.**

**Letters 5, 6 and 1 give us a word for a religious wrongdoing.**

**Letters 5, 7, 3 and 2 give us a word for "not different".**

| | | | | | | |
|---|---|---|---|---|---|---|
| 1 | 2 | 3 | 4 | 5 | 6 | 7 |

# MYSTERY SUDOKU

Complete the grid so that every row, column and 3 × 3 box contains the letters WORMTHUGS in any order. One row or column contains a six-letter word that is a fundamental process in gardening.

| | G | | | | | | W | T |
|---|---|---|---|---|---|---|---|---|
| | M | T | | | | | H | |
| | U | | | W | | | | G |
| | | W | R | | | | | M |
| | O | U | | | R | | | |
| | | | H | S | | | | W |
| | R | | | T | | | | S |
| | H | W | | | | G | | |
| S | | | | | | | M | U |

# BETWEEN THE LINES

A word used to describe certain plants – especially grasses – can be inserted in the blank line so that, reading downwards, ten three-letter words are formed. What is the hidden word between the lines?

| C | F | E | B | E | M | G | S | P | A |
|---|---|---|---|---|---|---|---|---|---|
|   |   |   |   |   |   |   |   |   |   |
| P | Y | D | G | U | N | U | Y | L | L |

# CROSS OUT

Cross out all the letters that appear more than once. The letters that are left, reading from left to right and top to bottom, will spell out some garden pests.

| B | T | A | J | K | T | P | Y |
|---|---|---|---|---|---|---|---|
| J | Y | K | H | Q | Y | B | M |
| K | M | Z | Q | F | I | Z | D |
| T | B | S | K | Y | J | F | M |

# WORD SEARCH: TULIPS

```
R  L  C  F  Y  E  P  S  T  F  V  J  M  J  N
J  U  Q  Z  D  R  L  Q  S  H  I  U  F  A  J
A  H  R  O  N  A  L  D  O  F  H  Y  N  J  F
C  S  U  F  T  I  V  A  I  E  Z  I  X  X  S
U  E  Y  Q  W  V  Q  L  J  F  J  H  B  G  S
Z  U  Q  N  N  A  F  W  Q  B  U  V  F  W  E
Z  M  G  I  Z  C  N  D  T  Q  A  U  I  E  R
I  Q  Z  W  L  E  K  F  J  D  Y  D  L  H  T
P  V  P  A  R  Y  M  L  A  P  F  A  Y  X  S
Z  S  O  Q  F  I  T  A  N  Q  D  M  G  Q  I
R  E  Q  U  E  S  T  H  Q  E  I  V  V  A  M
L  F  P  B  V  U  O  Y  G  X  S  Z  H  F  S
F  K  E  U  S  Q  L  D  X  L  J  Q  Z  P  G
C  D  T  M  E  D  I  L  A  G  U  S  C  M  Y
B  A  L  L  E  R  I  N  A  L  E  Q  X  E  N
```

Find the following varieties of tulip in the grid below.

| | | |
|---|---|---|
| BALLERINA | RIDGEDALE | CAVIAR |
| PALMYRA | JINAN | JACUZZI |
| REQUEST | RONALDO | MISTRESS |

# CROSSWORD: BEANS & PEAS

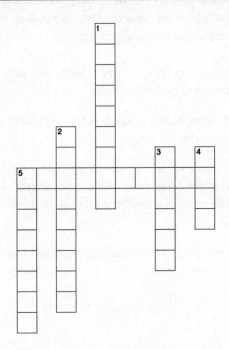

## ACROSS

**5.** Known as "white Italian beans" (10)

## DOWN

**1.** Peas in pop group? (5, 4)

**2.** French for "eat all" (9)

**3.** Internal organ (6)

**4.** Capital of Peru (4)

**5.** Key ingredient in hummus (8)

# TRIVIA

The Alnwick Garden in Northumberland, UK, has a tourist attraction with the ominous tagline: "Do you dare to enter?" What is the garden's ghastly attraction?

a) "The Poison Garden" – filled with around 100 toxic, intoxicating and narcotic plants

b) "The Gas Greenhouse" – a collection of global plants that emit noxious gases

c) "The Death House" – detailing horticultural deaths throughout the ages, from farmhands sliced by scythes to modern-day gardeners with digits missing from gardening mishaps

d) "The Cactus Lounge" – encouraging blindfolded visitors to touch the spiny plants to test their pain levels

# PAIRS GAME

Match up the 20 suns in 20 seconds. The first one has been done for you.

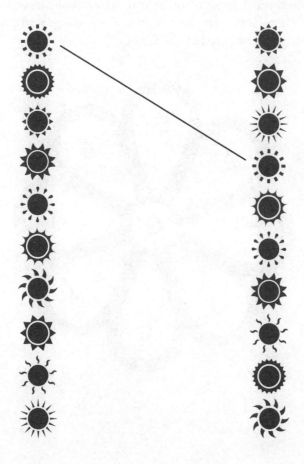

# WORD FLOWER

Do you like a spot of heavy landscaping? See how many words of four or more letters you can make from the letters below. All words must include the central letter, and proper nouns don't count! Also, can you find a word relating to garden landscaping that uses all the letters?

# MAZE

Can you get from the right-hand side to the middle of this hedge maze in under 60 seconds?

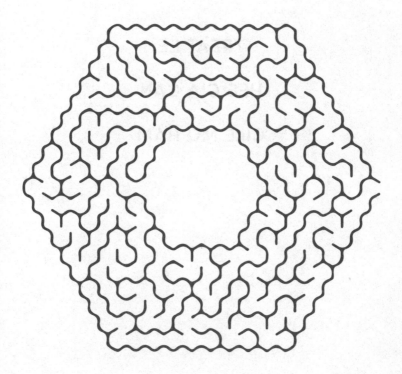

# ANAGRAMS: DOCTOR'S CALL

Rearrange these letters to reveal flowers or plants noted for their medicinal benefits.

TREAT EE

HEE CIA CAN

CILE MO HAM

# WORD LADDER

Most gardeners know what a "node" is, but in this word ladder can you change one letter at a time to turn the word "muse" into "node"?

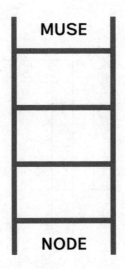

# CROSSWORD: PLANT DISEASES

## ACROSS

**3.** Arid decomposition (3, 3)

**4.** Spoils or damages (6)

**5.** Powdery or downy (6)

## DOWN

**1.** An iron oxide (4)

**2.** Hard coating on skin (4)

**3.** Tree from the Netherlands? (5, 3)

# COUNTING CONUNDRUM

🌹🌹 + 🌹🌹 + 🌹🌹 = 36

(🌼🌼 × 🌹🌹) + 🌹🌹 = 228

🍎 + (🌼 × 🍎) = 50

🍎🍎 + (🌹 × 🌼🌼) = ?

# DOWN THE MIDDLE

Complete all the following words correctly to reveal, in the shaded squares, an act that will be familiar to most gardeners.

| C | E |  | A | R |
| S | T |  | L | L |
| L | I |  | H | T |
| B | U |  | G | Y |
| B | R |  | S | K |
| L | O |  | E | R |
| B | U |  | L | E |

# WORD SEARCH: BIRDS GOING NUTS

| L | F | Z | T | P | R | G | E | Y | F | G | P | O | J | T |
|---|---|---|---|---|---|---|---|---|---|---|---|---|---|---|
| I | I | P | S | C | K | W | R | K | X | E | L | C | T | B |
| Y | Z | X | E | C | W | V | A | E | I | F | F | Y | I | L |
| S | P | A | R | R | O | W | K | K | A | Z | O | Z | X | A |
| R | E | X | C | A | M | I | E | R | S | T | A | R | S | C |
| B | U | H | D | S | N | B | F | N | X | D | T | C | N | K |
| G | K | C | L | P | K | O | U | G | B | X | B | I | N | B |
| V | S | T | O | K | U | K | E | K | W | C | K | D | T | I |
| U | H | A | G | T | N | R | D | G | Q | S | U | U | K | R |
| R | H | H | R | K | X | K | T | G | I | X | W | H | U | D |
| F | B | T | B | C | N | R | X | S | H | P | N | U | D | J |
| H | Y | U | P | M | C | O | U | H | V | R | D | N | S | I |
| M | E | N | R | R | H | B | P | F | S | D | P | O | F | K |
| I | P | G | I | I | U | I | F | P | H | H | K | V | O | G |
| B | U | L | L | F | I | N | C | H | K | X | S | S | P | W |

In the grid, find the following birds commonly attracted by bird feeders.

| SPARROW | GOLDCREST | SISKIN |
|---------|-----------|--------|
| ROBIN | NUTHATCH | GREAT TIT |
| BULLFINCH | BLACKBIRD | WOOD PIGEON |

# ACROSTICS

Solve the clues correctly and the shaded squares will reveal a potato variety. What is it?

1. Type of cosmetic
2. Graduates (plural)
3. Improve
4. To drink
5. Mariner

| 1. | | | | | |
|----|--|--|--|--|--|
| 2. | | | | | |
| 3. | | | | | |
| 4. | | | | | |
| 5. | | | | | |

# TRIVIA

Test your general knowledge with this trio of name-related multiple-choice questions.

## 1. What is another name for the avocado?

a) Snake stone plant
b) Crocodile fruit
c) Alligator pear

## 2. What is also known as a "love apple"?

a) Radish
b) Tomato
c) Redcurrant

## 3. What is also known as a "Chinese gooseberry"?

a) Lychee
b) Kiwi fruit
c) Dragon fruit

# GARDENING WORDS

Here is the last list of horticultural definitions. How's your knowledge?

### 1. VOLATILIZATION
a) The production of hydrogen
b) The process by which certain flowers compete for optimal growing conditions
c) The production of toxic gases by leaves

### 2. ANEMOPHILY
a) Pollination by wind
b) The propensity of plants to wilt in severe conditions
c) Any plants that thrive in extreme heat

### 3. CALYX
a) Collective name for sepals of a flower
b) Collective name for petals of a flower
c) Collective name for ovules of a flower

# SPOT THE
# DIFFERENCE

Can you spot the five differences between the two pictures?

# WORD GROWER

The letters of a seven-letter word have been numbered 1 to 7. Solve the clues to reveal a word used to describe certain species of roses.

**Letters 2, 5 and 6 give us a type of beer.**

**Letters 7, 2 and 3 give us a male sheep.**

**Letters 4, 2, 1 and 6 give us a word for "empty".**

| | | | | | | |
|---|---|---|---|---|---|---|
| 1 | 2 | 3 | 4 | 5 | 6 | 7 |

# MYSTERY SUDOKU

Complete the grid so that every row, column and 3 × 3 box contains the letters LOFIGAREV in any order. One row or column contains a six-letter word that is a material used in many gardens.

|   |   |   |   |   |   | R |   |   |
|---|---|---|---|---|---|---|---|---|
| I | F |   |   | G | R | V |   |   |
|   |   |   |   |   |   |   | A | E |
| L | V |   | I |   |   |   | G |   |
| O |   | G |   |   |   |   | L |   |
| F |   |   |   | E |   |   |   |   |
| V | E |   |   | R |   |   |   |   |
|   |   | I |   |   | O |   | R |   |
|   |   | O | F | V | I |   | E |   |

# BETWEEN
# THE LINES

A poison-producing plant can be inserted in the blank line so that, reading downwards, nine three-letter words are formed. What is the hidden word between the lines?

| O | S | E | B | A | S | I | W | U |
|---|---|---|---|---|---|---|---|---|
|   |   |   |   |   |   |   |   |   |
| D | N | G | D | E | G | L | N | E |

# DOUBLE TAKE

The names of some things found in a garden often have more than one meaning. So, for example, the answer to the clue "slough off (4)" would be "shed". Solve the clues below and name the things found in a garden. The number of letters in the answer is given in parentheses.

1. Conspiracy (4)

2. Newspaper articles (9)

3. Dividing line (6)

4. Pages (5)

5. Ghost (5)

# ANSWERS

## 1. Word Search: In the Herb Garden

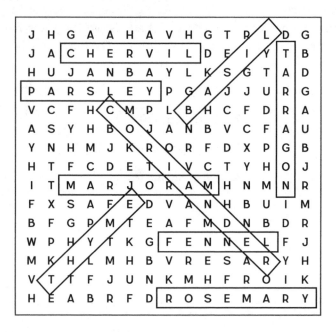

## 2. Crossword: Flowers & Plants

1 monkey puzzle, 2 forget-me-not, 3 wallflower, 4 chrysanthemum, 5 runner bean, 6 narcissus

## 3. Trivia

1 c), 2 b), 3 c), 4 a)

## 4. Pairs Game

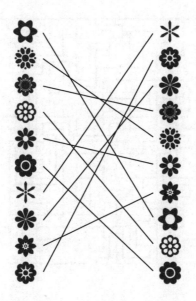

## 5. Word Flower
Word that uses all letters = aubergine

## 6. Maze

## 7. Anagrams: Gardening Tools
Pruning shears, watering hose, wheelbarrow, hand trowel,
leaf blower

## 8. Word Ladder
One possible solution: sale, sole, pole, pope, rope, rose

## 9. Crossword: Types of Plants
1 climber, 2 succulent, 3 cactus, 4 bamboo, 5 perennial, 6 alpine

## 10. Counting Conundrum
Trowel = 20, pot = 5, watering can = 2, trowel + pot + watering can
= 27

## 11. Riddle
Potato

## 12. Word Search: Eat Your Greens

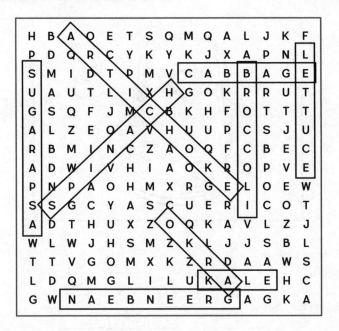

## 13. Acrostics

1 ballet, 2 launch, 3 Apollo, 4 caviar, 5 kitten. The letters in the shaded squares spell "blackthorn".

## 14. Trivia

1 b), 2 c)

## 15. Gardening Words

1 b), 2 c), 3 b)

## 16. Spot the Difference

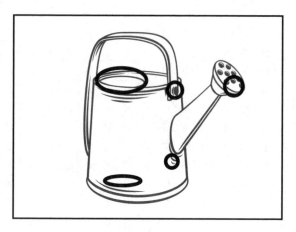

## 17. Word Grower

Juniper

## 18. Mystery Sudoku

| L | E | S | C | R | F | O | D | W |
|---|---|---|---|---|---|---|---|---|
| D | O | R | E | L | W | F | S | C |
| W | C | F | S | D | O | L | E | R |
| O | S | L | D | W | C | E | R | F |
| C | F | W | R | S | E | D | O | L |
| R | D | E | O | F | L | C | W | S |
| F | L | O | W | E | R | S | C | D |
| E | R | D | F | C | S | W | L | O |
| S | W | C | L | O | D | R | F | E |

## 19. Between the Lines
Compost

## 20. Missing Words
Marrow, pea, paving

## 21. Word Search: In Bloom

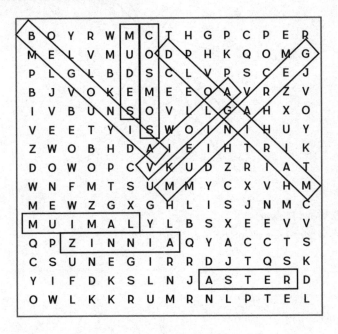

## 22. Crossword: Garden Visitors – Mammals
1 mole, 2 hedgehog, 3 mouse, 4 badger, 5 squirrel, 6 rabbit

## 23. Trivia
1 c), 2 b)

## 24. Pairs Game

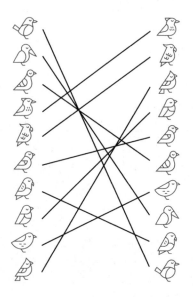

## 25. Word Flower

Word that uses all letters = euphorbia

## 26. Maze

## 27. Anagrams: Genera
Crocus, freesia, gladiolus

## 28. Word Ladder
One possible solution: hall, half, calf, calm, palm

## 29. Crossword: Animal Magic
1 foxglove, 2 cowslip, 3 dogwood, 4 ponytail, 5 catnip, 6 crab apple

## 30. Counting Conundrum
Wheelbarrow = 6, lawnmower = 7, fence = 12

## 31. Word Link
1 game, 2 moon, 3 hawk, 4 peer, 5 port. The word in the shaded column is "mower".

## 32. Word Search: Know Your Onions

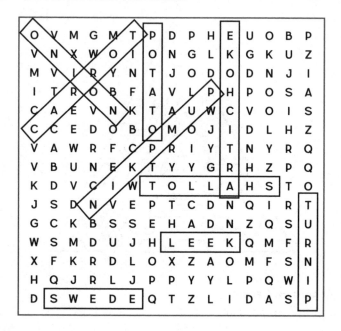

## 33. Acrostics

1 ballad, 2 embryo, 3 lardon, 4 lesson, 5 Aurora. The letters in the shaded squares spell "belladonna".

## 34. Trivia

1 a), 2 c)

## 35. Gardening Words

1 c), 2 a), 3 c)

## 36. Spot the Difference

## 37. Word Grower
Begonia

## 38. Mystery Sudoku

| O | N | S | I | R | D | B | A | G |
|---|---|---|---|---|---|---|---|---|
| R | G | A | O | B | S | I | N | D |
| I | D | B | A | N | G | R | O | S |
| S | B | I | N | G | O | D | R | A |
| N | O | G | D | A | R | S | I | B |
| A | R | D | B | S | I | O | G | N |
| G | I | R | S | D | A | N | B | O |
| D | A | N | R | O | B | G | S | I |
| B | S | O | G | I | N | A | D | R |

## 39. Between the Lines
Ladybird

## 40. Hidden Tools
1 fork, 2 shears, 3 trowel, 4 rake, 5 spade

## 41. Word Search: Let It Grow

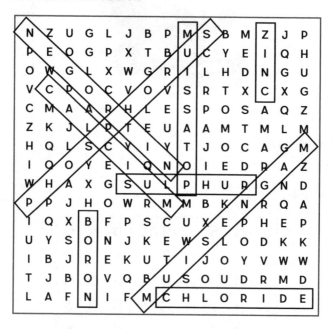

## 42. Crossword: Herbs
1 thyme, 2 tarragon, 3 parsley, 4 dill, 5 basil

## 43. Trivia
1 lawnmowers, 2 flowerpots, 3 secateurs and pruners, 4 spades,
5 electric hedge trimmers, 6 plant tubs and troughs, 7 shears,
8 garden forks, 9 hoses and sprinklers, 10 garden canes and sticks

## 44. Pairs Game

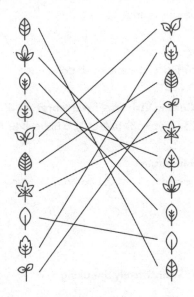

## 45. Word Flower
Word that uses all letters = spearmint

## 46. Maze

### 47. Anagrams: Fruity

Plum, olive, cucumber, orange

### 48. Word Ladder

One possible solution: jest, pest, post, pose, hose

### 49. Crossword: Garden Visitors – Invertebrates

1 snail, 2 earwig, 3 ladybird, 4 butterfly, 5 honeybee, 6 greenfly

### 50. Counting Conundrum

Sun = 10, bird = 4, bird house = 2, bird house + (sun × bird) = 42

### 51. Riddle

Topiary

### 52. Word Search: Scientifically Speaking

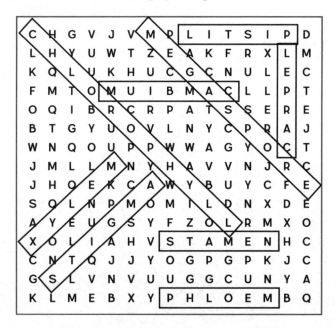

### 53. Acrostics

1 global, 2 Oporto, 3 lactic, 4 dik-dik, 5 idiots. The letters in the shaded squares spell "Goldilocks".

### 54. Trivia

b)

### 55. Gardening Words

1 b), 2 b), 3 b)

### 56. Spot the Difference

### 57. Word Grower

Hardcore

## 58. Mystery Sudoku

| U | W | L | A | B | O | R | T | E |
|---|---|---|---|---|---|---|---|---|
| T | R | O | W | E | L | B | U | A |
| A | E | B | U | R | T | W | O | L |
| W | A | R | B | U | E | O | L | T |
| B | L | U | O | T | W | A | E | R |
| O | T | E | R | L | A | U | B | W |
| E | B | A | T | W | U | L | R | O |
| R | O | T | L | A | B | E | W | U |
| L | U | W | E | O | R | T | A | B |

## 59. Between the Lines

Heather

## 60. Missing Plant

Agave

## 61. Word Search: Garden Critters

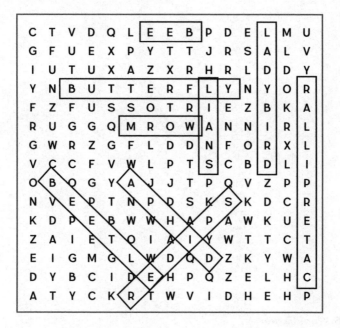

## 62. Crossword: Garden Features

1 pergola, 2 veranda, 3 gazebo, 4 fountain, 5 topiary, 6 trellis

## 63. Trivia

1 a), 2 c), 3 b)

## 64. Pairs Game

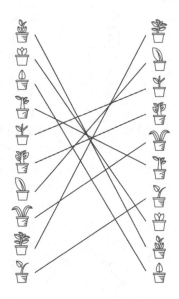

## 65. Word Flower

Word that uses all letters = mayflower

## 66. Maze

## 67. Anagrams: A Little Help

Beetle, spider, hoverfly, lacewing

## 68. Word Ladder

One possible solution: meal, heal, heap, leap, leaf

## 69. Crossword: Popular Flowers

1 iris, 2 (down) lilac, 2 (across) lily, 3 daisy, 4 rose, 5 snapdragon

## 70. Counting Conundrum

Spray bottle = 6, hose = 7

## 71. Mini Sudoku: Spring

| R | G | I | N | P | S |
|---|---|---|---|---|---|
| N | S | P | I | R | G |
| I | R | S | G | N | P |
| P | N | G | S | I | R |
| G | I | R | P | S | N |
| S | P | N | R | G | I |

## 72. Word Search: Housing Plants

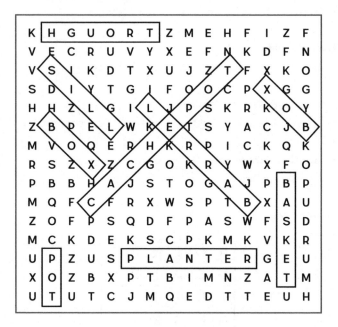

## 73. Acrostics

1 rapier, 2 uncurb, 3 native, 4 nausea, 5 eleven. The letters in the shaded squares spell "runner bean".

## 74. Trivia

1 b), 2 a), 3 c)

## 75. Gardening Words

1 a), 2 c), 3 b)

## 76. Spot the Difference

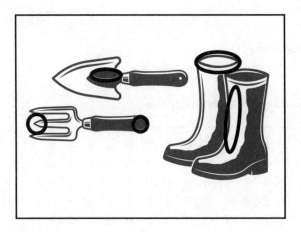

## 77. Word Grower

Decking

## 78. Mystery Sudoku

| M | N | G | R | A | I | T | W | O |
|---|---|---|---|---|---|---|---|---|
| O | T | I | G | M | W | R | A | N |
| W | A | R | T | O | N | M | G | I |
| I | O | T | M | W | A | N | R | G |
| N | M | W | O | R | G | I | T | A |
| G | R | A | N | I | T | W | O | M |
| T | I | O | A | N | R | G | M | W |
| R | W | M | I | G | O | A | N | T |
| A | G | N | W | T | M | O | I | R |

### 79. Between the Lines
Camellia

### 80. How Many?
31 (including the four in the question)

### 81. Word Search: Global Emblems

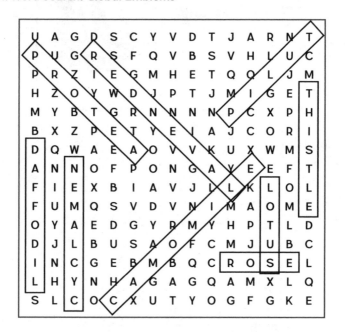

### 82. Crossword: Pollination
1 pistil, 2 receptacle, 3 style, 4 stamen, 5 stigma, 6 filament

### 83. Trivia: Strange But True
1 b), 2 c)

## 84. Pairs Game

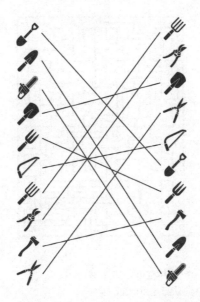

## 85. Word Flower

Word that uses all letters = sunflower

## 86. Maze

## 87. Anagrams: Tree Shapes
Conical, round headed, pendulous

## 88. Word Ladder
One possible solution: doer, door, doom, room, root

## 89. Crossword: Sports Played on a Freshly Mown Lawn
1 cricket, 2 croquet, 3 tennis, 4 (down) boules, 4 (across) badminton, 5 bowls

## 90. Counting Conundrum
Spade = 10, secateurs = 5, fork = 2, secateurs + (fork × secateurs) = 15

## 91. Down the Middle
Garden

## 92. Word Search: In the Allotment

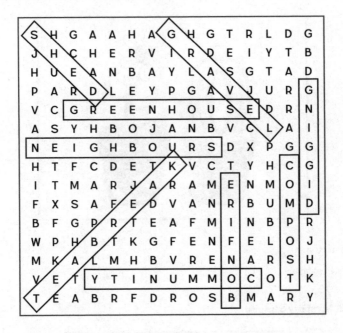

## 93. Acrostics

1 exotic, 2 raffle, 3 indigo, 4 cachou, 5 abacus. The letters in the shaded squares spell "ericaceous".

## 94. Trivia

1 c), 2 b), 3 b)

## 95. Gardening Words

1 b), 2 a), 3 c)

## 96. Spot the Difference

## 97. Word Grower

Hydrangea

## 98. Mystery Sudoku

| N | I | S | G | T | E | R | A | W |
|---|---|---|---|---|---|---|---|---|
| G | A | T | R | W | N | S | E | I |
| W | E | R | I | A | S | N | G | T |
| I | G | E | N | S | W | T | R | A |
| S | W | A | T | E | R | I | N | G |
| R | T | N | A | I | G | W | S | E |
| A | R | I | S | G | T | E | W | N |
| T | S | W | E | N | A | G | I | R |
| E | N | G | W | R | I | A | T | S |

## 99. Between the Lines

Hardiness

## 100. Cross Out

Flower

## 101. Word Search: Exotic Plants

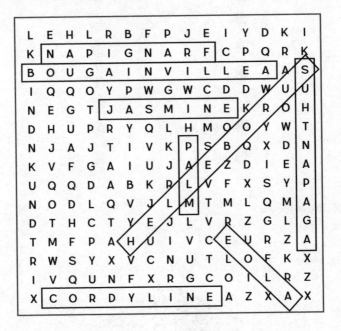

## 102. Crossword: Traditional Meanings of Flower Colours

1 blue, 2 yellow, 3 green, 4 purple, 5 red, 6 orange

## 103. Trivia

a)

## 104. Pairs Game

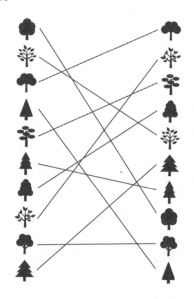

## 105. Word Flower
Plant that uses all letters = wild pansy

## 106. Maze

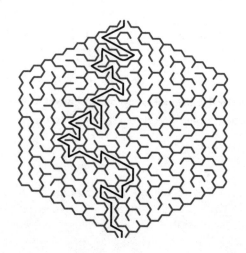

### 107. Anagrams: Propagation
Cuttings, layering, grafting

### 108. Word Ladder
One possible solution: sold, cold, cord, ford, fork

### 109. Crossword: A Mixed Bunch
1 willow, 2 ginger, 3 magnolia, 4 pepper

### 110. Counting Conundrum
Butterfly = 8, ant = 9, snail = 4

### 111. Riddles
1 pea, 2 potato

### 112. Word Search: Climbers

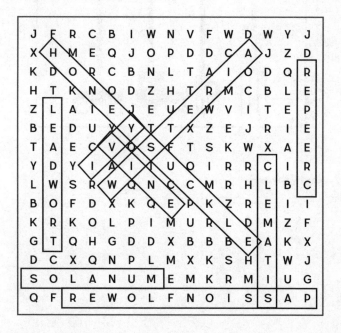

## 113. Acrostics

1 tackle, 2 unthaw, 3 mirage, 4 Belize, 5 lizard. The letters in the shaded squares spell "tumbleweed".

## 114. Trivia

b), c), e)

## 115. Gardening Words

1 a), 2 b), 3 c)

## 116. Spot the Difference

## 117. Word Grower

Alkaline

## 118. Mystery Sudoku

| U | G | N | T | S | I | L | O | H |
|---|---|---|---|---|---|---|---|---|
| S | H | I | L | U | O | T | N | G |
| L | T | O | G | N | H | S | U | I |
| H | N | S | U | L | T | G | I | O |
| G | L | U | O | I | S | H | T | N |
| I | O | T | H | G | N | U | S | L |
| O | I | G | S | H | U | N | L | T |
| N | S | L | I | T | G | O | H | U |
| T | U | H | N | O | L | I | G | S |

## 119. Between the Lines

Conifer

## 120. Hidden Flowers

1 daisy, 2 orchid, 3 azalea, 4 crocus, 5 iris

## 121. Word Search: Latin Names

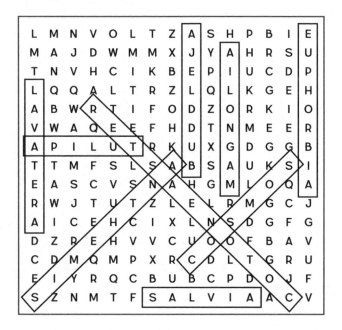

## 122. Crossword: Garden Critters

1 spider, 2 centipede, 3 earthworm, 4 caterpillar, 5 slug, 6 crane fly

## 123. Trivia

d)

## 124. Pairs Game

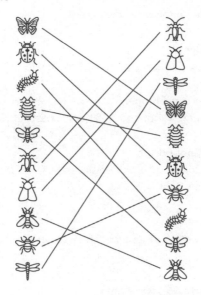

## 125. Word Flower
Word that uses all letters = artichoke

## 126. Maze

### 127. Anagrams
Bird bath, garden gnome, wind chime

### 128. Word Ladder
One possible solution: ping, pint, lint, line, lime

### 129. Crossword: Tree Sample
1 ash, 2 holly, 3 elm, 4 mahogany, 5 horse chestnut, 6 pine

### 130. Counting Conundrum
Boot = 4, single glove = 10, pair of gloves = 20, shears = 9, pair of gloves + (shears × boot) = 56

### 131. Word Link
1 late, 2 slum, 3 cult, 4 trip, 5 pipe. The word in the shaded column is "tulip".

### 132. Word Search: Aquatic Plants

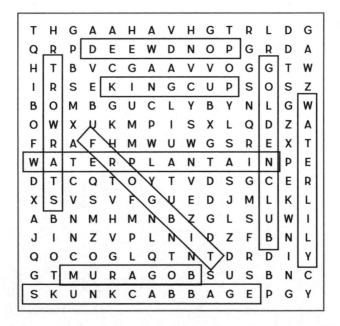

## 133. Acrostics

1 sister, 2 nebula, 3 airbag, 4 pedalo, 5 damson. The letters in the shaded squares spell "snapdragon".

## 134. Trivia

b)

## 135. Gardening Words

1 b), 2 a), 3 b)

## 136. Spot the Difference

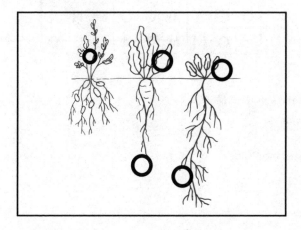

## 137. Word Grower

Botrytis

## 138. Mystery Sudoku

| G | A | R | M | O | C | N | I | U |
|---|---|---|---|---|---|---|---|---|
| C | O | I | A | U | N | G | R | M |
| U | M | N | G | I | R | A | O | C |
| R | N | C | U | A | G | O | M | I |
| A | U | O | C | M | I | R | G | N |
| M | I | G | R | N | O | C | U | A |
| N | R | U | O | C | M | I | A | G |
| O | C | A | I | G | U | M | N | R |
| I | G | M | N | R | A | U | C | O |

## 139. Between the Lines

Nutrients

## 140. Missing Plant

Peony

## 141. Word Search: Beautiful Landscapes

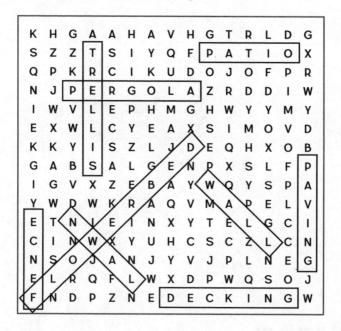

## 142. Crossword: In the Woods

1 toadstool, 2 glade, 3 copse, 4 evergreen, 5 woodpecker, 6 bramble

## 143. Trivia

d)

## 144. Pairs Game

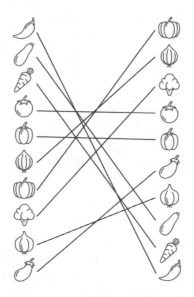

## 145. Word Flower
Word that uses all letters = goldfinch

## 146. Maze

## 147. Anagrams: Something Shrubbery
Erect, round, spreading

## 148. Word Ladder
One possible solution: boar, soar, sear, seat, peat

## 149. Crossword: Photosynthesis Words
1 chlorophyll, 2 water, 3 carbohydrate, 4 carbon dioxide, 5 oxygen,
6 light

## 150. Counting Conundrum
Chainsaw = 20, handsaw = 16, axe = 13, chainsaw +
(axe × handsaw) = 228

## 151. Mini Sudoku: Winter

| R | T | I | E | W | N |
|---|---|---|---|---|---|
| N | W | E | R | T | I |
| T | N | R | I | E | W |
| E | I | W | N | R | T |
| W | R | N | T | I | E |
| I | E | T | W | N | R |

## 152. Word Search

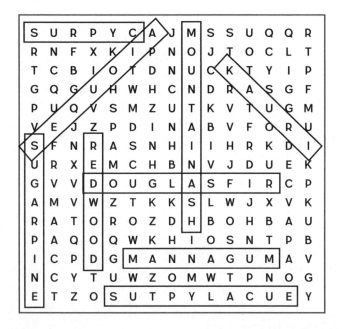

## 153. Acrostics
1 Cancer, 2 orange, 3 napkin, 4 fabric, 5 edible. The letters in the shaded squares spell "Conference".

### 154. Trivia
b)

### 155. Gardening Words
1 b), 2 b), 3 c)

### 156. Spot the Difference

### 157. Word Grower
Greenhouse

### 158. Mystery Sudoku

| P | R | O | D | U | C | E | A | L |
|---|---|---|---|---|---|---|---|---|
| C | U | L | P | E | A | R | D | O |
| D | E | A | R | O | L | U | C | P |
| U | C | R | L | D | P | A | O | E |
| O | A | D | E | R | U | L | P | C |
| L | P | E | A | C | O | D | R | U |
| E | O | C | U | A | R | P | L | D |
| A | D | P | C | L | E | O | U | R |
| R | L | U | O | P | D | C | E | A |

### 159. Between the Lines
Geranium

### 160. How Many?
18 (including the five in the question and heading)

### 161. Word Search: In the Garden

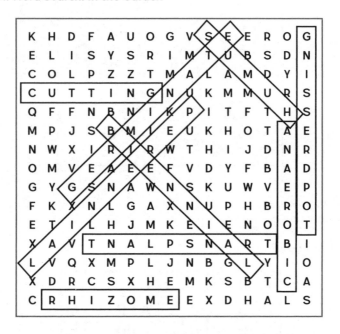

### 162. Crossword: Saying It with Flowers
1 carnation, 2 marigold, 3 hydrangea, 4 rose, 5 hibiscus, 6 tulip

### 163. Trivia
b)

## 164. Pairs Game

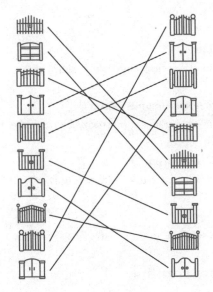

## 165. Word Flower
Herb that uses all letters = wild thyme

## 166. Maze

### 167. Anagrams: Female Names

Daphne, erica, primrose

### 168. Word Ladder

One possible solution: clap, clam, slam, slum, plum

### 169. Crossword: Flavoursome Plants

1 fennel, 2 liquorice, 3 garlic, 4 rosemary, 5 angelica, 6 horseradish

### 170. Counting Conundrum

Rake = 9, fork = 3, leaf = 2, rake − (fork + leaf) + 1 = 5

### 171. Riddles

1 their feet, 2 a seed

### 172. Word Search: In the Red

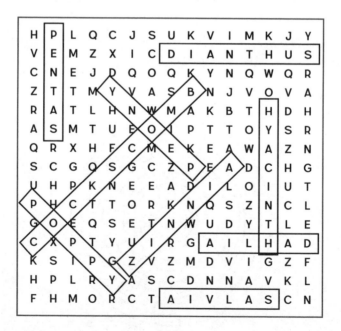

### 173. Acrostics

1 bicarb, 2 Lassie, 3 archer, 4 condor, 5 kidney. The letters in the shaded squares spell "blackberry".

### 174. Trivia

c)

### 175. Gardening Words

1 a), 2 c), 3 b)

### 176. Spot the Difference

### 177. Word Grower

Nemesia

## 178. Mystery Sudoku

| O | G | S | R | M | H | U | W | T |
|---|---|---|---|---|---|---|---|---|
| W | R | M | T | G | U | S | H | O |
| H | T | U | S | O | W | M | R | G |
| S | H | T | O | W | R | G | U | M |
| M | W | O | U | T | G | R | S | H |
| R | U | G | M | H | S | O | T | W |
| G | M | R | H | U | T | W | O | S |
| U | O | H | W | S | M | T | G | R |
| T | S | W | G | R | O | H | M | U |

## 179. Between the Lines

Ornamental

## 180. Cross Out

Aphids

## 181. Word Search: Tulips

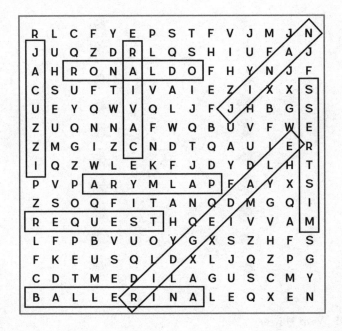

## 182. Crossword: Beans & Peas

1 black eyed, 2 mangetout, 3 kidney, 4 lima, 5 (down) chickpea,
5 (across) cannellini

## 183. Trivia

a)

## 184. Pairs Game

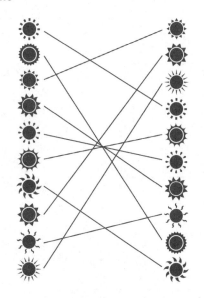

## 185. Word Flower

Word that uses all letters = flagstone

## 186. Maze

## 187. Anagrams: Doctor's Call

Tea tree, echinacea, chamomile

## 188. Word Ladder

One possible solution: muse, ruse, rude, nude, node

## 189. Crossword: Plant Diseases

1 rust, 2 scab, 3 (down) Dutch elm, 3 (across) dry rot, 4 blight, 5 mildew

## 190. Counting Conundrum

Rose = 6, daisy = 9, apple = 5, two apples + (rose × two daisies) = 118

## 191. Down the Middle

Digging

## 192. Word Search: Birds Going Nuts

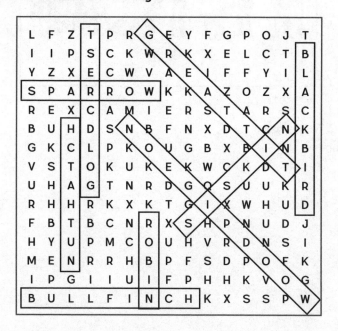

### 193. Acrostics

1 makeup, 2 alumni, 3 revamp, 4 imbibe, 5 sailor. The letters in the shaded squares spell "Maris Piper".

### 194. Trivia

1 c), 2 b), 3 b)

### 195. Gardening Words

1 c), 2 a), 3 a)

### 196. Spot the Difference

### 197. Word Grower

Rambler

## 198. Mystery Sudoku

| E | O | L | V | I | A | R | F | G |
|---|---|---|---|---|---|---|---|---|
| I | F | A | E | G | R | V | O | L |
| G | R | V | O | F | L | I | A | E |
| L | V | E | I | O | F | A | G | R |
| O | I | G | R | A | V | E | L | F |
| F | A | R | G | L | E | O | V | I |
| V | E | F | A | R | G | L | I | O |
| A | G | I | L | E | O | F | R | V |
| R | L | O | F | V | I | G | E | A |

## 199. Between the Lines

Digitalis

## 200. Double Take

1 plot, 2 clippings, 3 border, 4 leaves, 5 shade

Have you enjoyed this book? If so, find us on Facebook at **Summersdale Publishers**, on Twitter at **@Summersdale** and on Instagram at **@summersdalebooks** and get in touch. We'd love to hear from you!

# www.summersdale.com